JUST GREAT SONGS

This publication is not authorised for sale in
the United States of America and/or Canada

WISE PUBLICATIONS
part of The Music Sales Group

London / New York / Paris / Sydney / Copenhagen / Berlin / Madrid / Tokyo

Published by
Wise Publications
14-15 Berners Street, London, W1T 3LJ, UK.

Exclusive distributors:
Music Sales Limited
Distribution Centre, Newmarket Road,
Bury St Edmunds, Suffolk, IP33 3YB, UK.

Music Sales Pty Limited
120 Rothschild Avenue, Rosebery,
NSW 2018, Australia.

Order No. AM991694
ISBN 978-1-84772-256-0
This book © Copyright 2007 Wise Publications,
a division of Music Sales Limited.

Edited by Rachel Payne.
Music arranged by Camden Music, Derek Jones & Artemis Music.
Music processed by Camden Music & Paul Ewers Music Design.

Printed in the EU.

BLACK AND WHITE TOWN

Words & Music by Jeremy Williams, Andrew Williams & Jamie Goodwin

Original key B♭ minor.

♩ = 172

N.C.

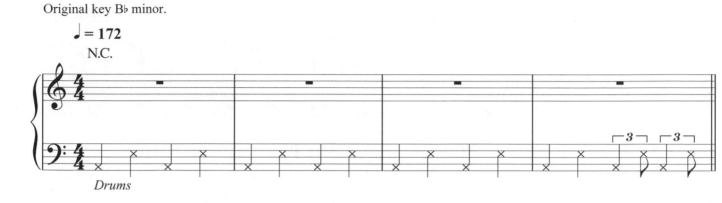

Drums

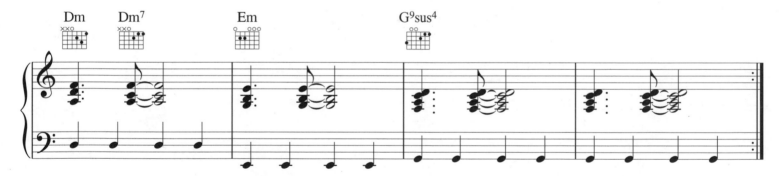

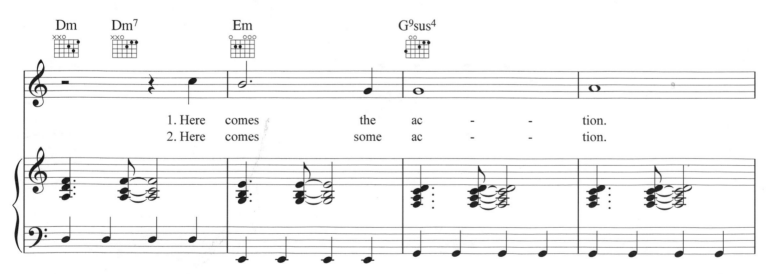

1. Here comes the ac - - tion.
2. Here comes some ac - - tion.

This is a dangerous place man. *This is a dangerous place, there's nothing here.*

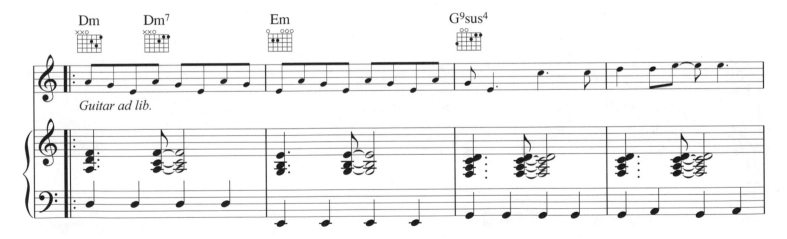

In a black and white_____ town.

Guitar ad lib.

9

I've been ten feet un - der - ground _____

— in the black and white _____ town. _____

Play 3 times ad lib.

AMERICA

Song by Johnny Borrell & Andy Burrows
Music by Razorlight

Con pedale

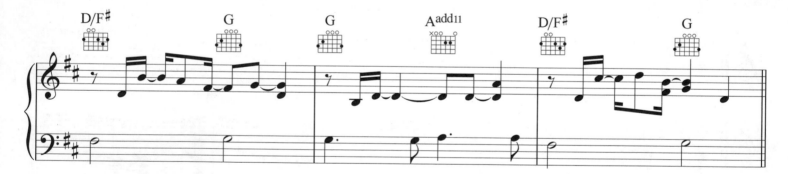

1. What a drag it is;___ the shape I'm in,___ and well, I go out some-where, then

14

no-thing on the T V, no - thing on the ra - di - o that means that much to me.___ There's

no-thing on the T V, no - thing on the ra - di - o that I can be - lieve___ in.

All my life,___ I'm watch-ing A - me - ri - ca.

All my life,___ there's pa - nic in A - me - ri - ca.

Oh, oh, oh,_____ oh. There's trou - ble in A - me - ri - ca.

Oh, oh, oh,_____ oh. There's pan - ic in A - me - ri - ca.

Oh, oh, oh,_____ oh._____

D.S. al Coda

BRINC ME TO LIFE

Words & Music by Ben Moody, Amy Lee & David Hodges

1. *(Female)* How can you see into my eyes, like o-pen doors? Lead-ing you down

into my core where I've be-come so numb.

(1.) With-out a soul,

2. Now that I know what I'm with-out

my spi-rit's sleep-ing some-where

you can't just leave me. Breathe

cold, un-til you find it there and lead

into me and make me real.

23

darling. On - ly you____ are____ the life____

a - mong____ the dead.____

(Male) All this____ time I can't be-lieve I could-n't see,

(F) I've been sleep-ing a thou - sand years____ it seems,

kept in the dark but you were there in front of me.

got to o - pen my eyes to ev - 'ry- thing.____

(M) With-out a thought, with-out a voice, with-out a soul.

Don't let me die here, there must be some - thing__ more. (Female)Bring

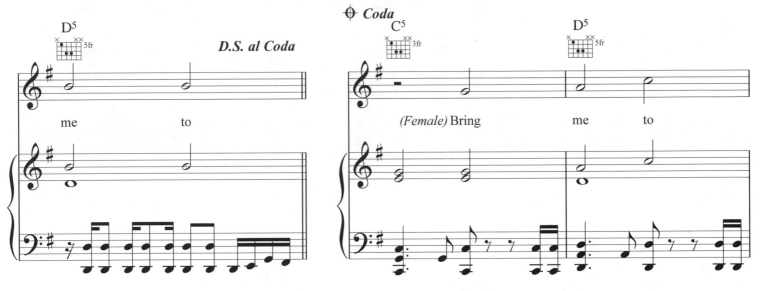

D.S. al Coda

Coda

me to

(Female) Bring me to

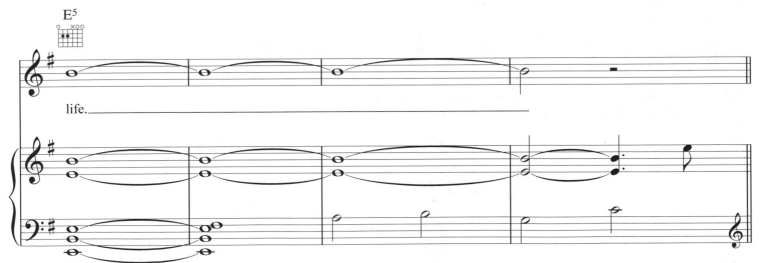

life.__

Repeat to fade

Come Away With Me

Words & Music by Norah Jones

1. Come a - way with me in the night.
2. Come a - way with me on a bus.

(Verses 5 & 6 Instrumental)

28

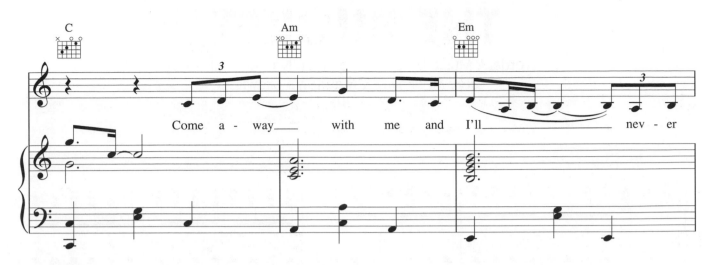

Come a - way___ with me and I'll___ nev - er

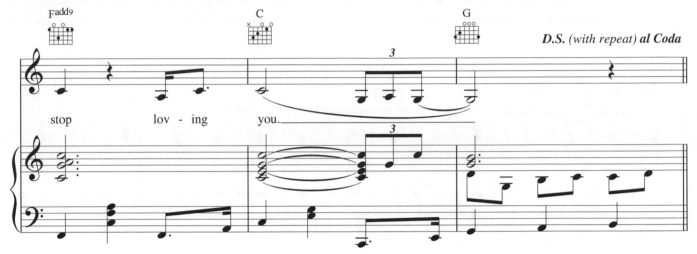

D.S. (with repeat) al Coda

stop lov - ing you.___

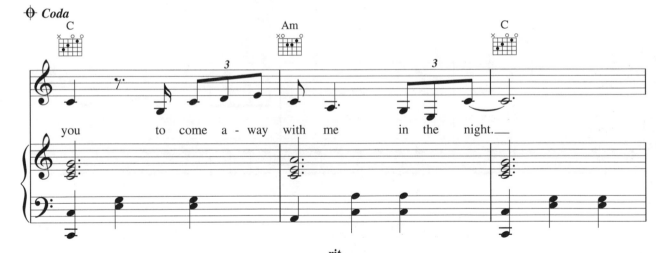

Coda

you to come a - way with me in the night.___

rit.

Come a - way_____ with me.

THE BUCKET

Words & Music by Caleb Followill, Nathan Followill,
Jared Followill & Matthew Followill

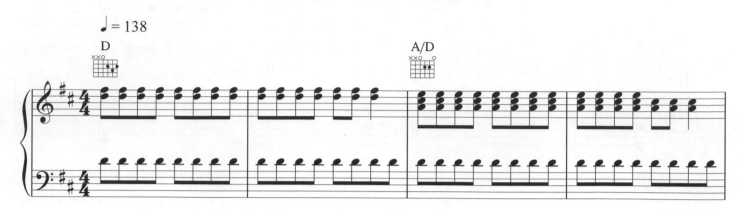

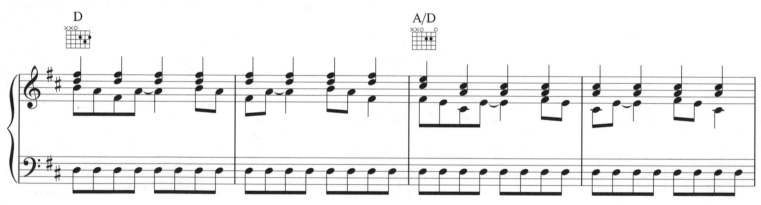

1. I'll

you get the zip-per fixed___ on my shoe, then I'll___ be in the lob-by drink-

-ways___ re-mem-ber the pact___ that we made,___ too___ young___ to die___ but old___

-ing for two.

___ is the grave.

Eight - een, bald - ing

star.

Gold - en, fall - en___

heart.___

1.

2. Look

2.

A/D   G/D   A/D   G/D

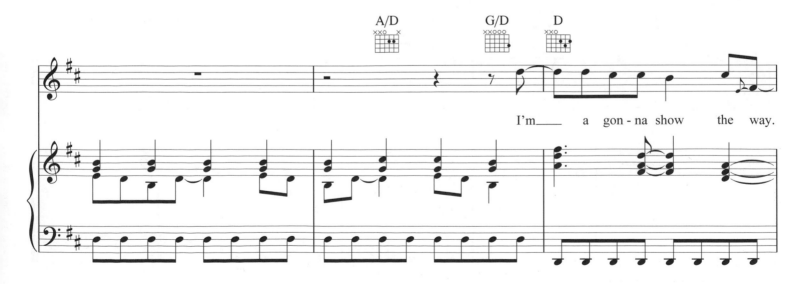

A/D   G/D   D

I'm___ a gon - na show the way.

I'm___ a gon-na show the way.___ I'm___

___ a gon-na show the way.___ I'm___ a gon-na show the way.___

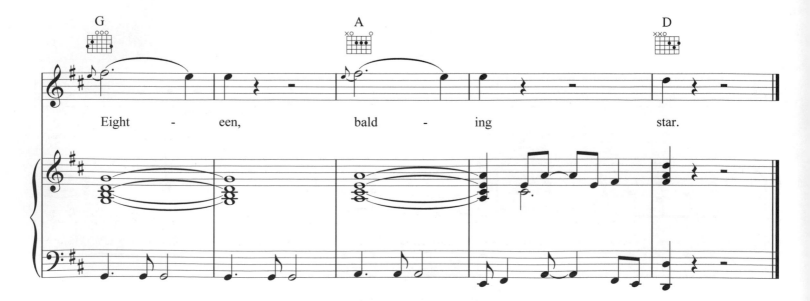

Eight - een, bald - ing star.

COUNTRY GIRL

Words & Music by Bobby Gillespie, Gary Mounfield, Martin Duffy & Andrew Innes

Medium Rock ♩ = 126

1. Nev - er get too big,

nev-er get too heav - y. Nev-er get too cool___ as you___ stop pay- in' your dues,___ oh, yeah.___

What can a poor boy do?___ Bet-ter go

back to your Mom-ma, she'll take care of you.

2. Lost your wife, lost your son.
3. Cra-zy wo-men mess your head. Wake
(4.) I have to say be-fore I have to go: be care-

Stay out drink-in' till morn-ing comes,
up drunk and bleed-in' in some strange bed, oh, yeah.
-ful with your seed, you'll reap just what you sow,

What can a poor boy do? Bet-ter go

back to your Mom-ma, she'll take care of you.____

Coun-try girl,_____ take__ my hand,__ lead__ me through__ this dis - eased land.__

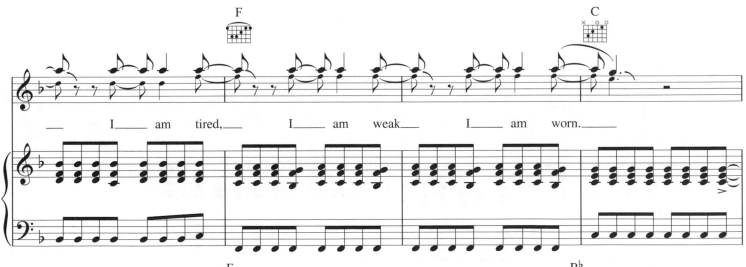

__ I__ am tired,__ I__ am weak__ I__ am worn.____

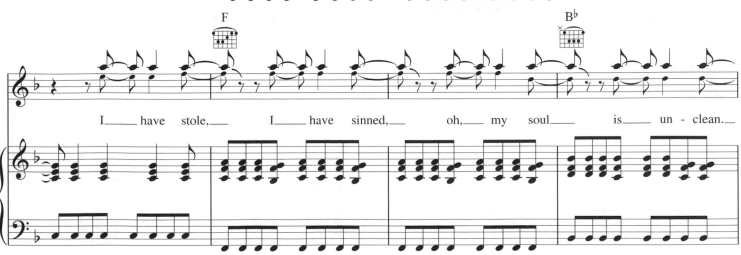

I__ have stole,__ I__ have sinned,__ oh,__ my soul__ is__ un - clean.__

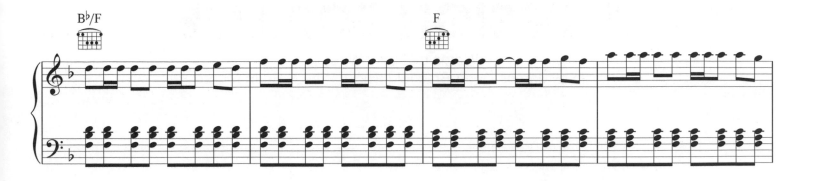

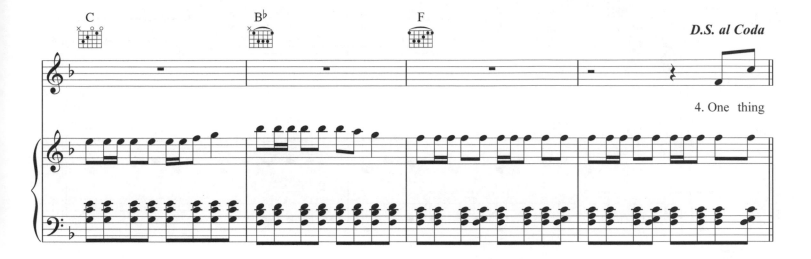

D.S. al Coda

4. One thing

Coun - try   girl,____   got____ to   keep____   ____ on keep - in'   on.____

A Design For Life

Words by Nicky Wire
Music by James Dean Bradfield, Nicky Wire & Sean Moore

for a shal - low piece of dig - ni - ty.
to show_____ from where I came.

1.　　　　　　　　　　　　2, 3.

2.I

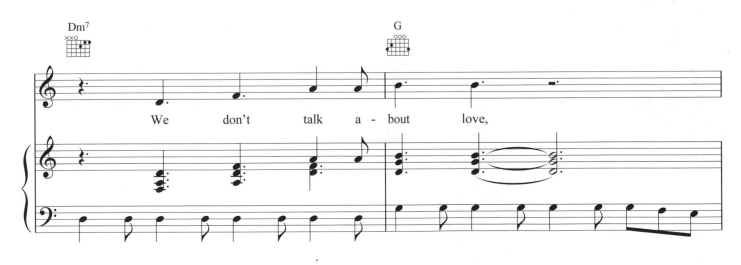

We don't talk a - bout love,

we on - ly want to get drunk,　　　　and we are not al -

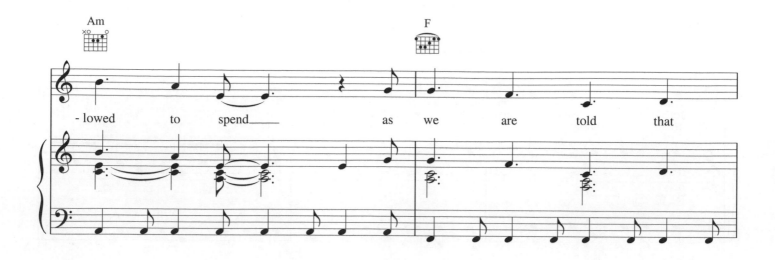

-lowed to spend_____ as we are told that

this is the end A de - sign

for_____ life, a de - sign for_____ life,

a de - sign for_____ life, a de - sign for

life.

3. I

⊕ **Coda**

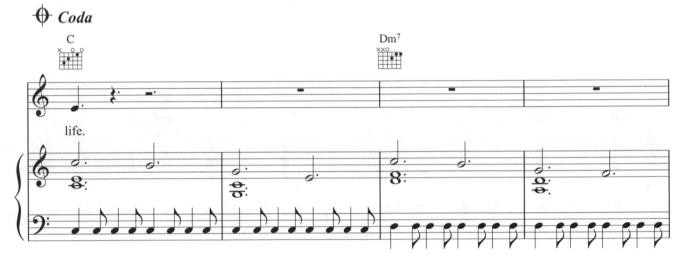

life.

We don't talk a - bout life, we on - ly want to

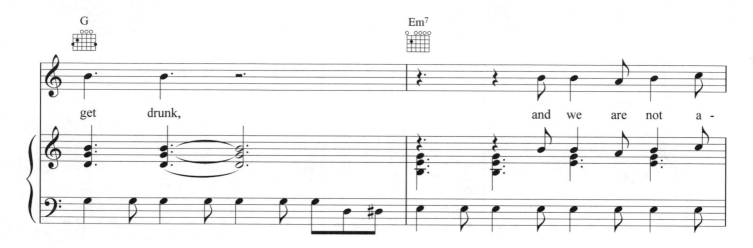

get drunk, and we are not a -

- lowed to spend_ as we are told that this is the end.

A de - sign for_____ life, a de - sign

for_____ life,   a   de - sign   for_____ life,

a   de - sign   for   life.

N.C.

Fadd⁹

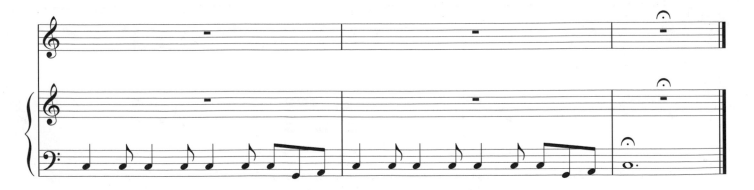

45

DRIFTWOOD

Words & Music by Fran Healy

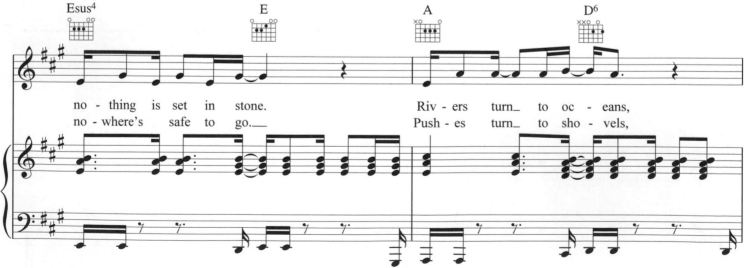

1. Ev-'ry - thing is op - en,
3. Ev - 'ry where there's trou - ble,

no - thing is set in stone. Riv - ers turn_ to oc - eans,
no - where's safe to go._ Push - es turn_ to sho - vels,

- wood,   but you've been drift - ing for a long, long   time.

You've been drift - ing for a long, long   time.

You've been drift - ing for a long, long,

drift - ing for a long, long   time.

DROPS OF JUPITER

**Words & Music by Jimmy Stafford, Scott Underwood,
Patrick Monahan, Robert Hotchkiss & Clifford Colin**

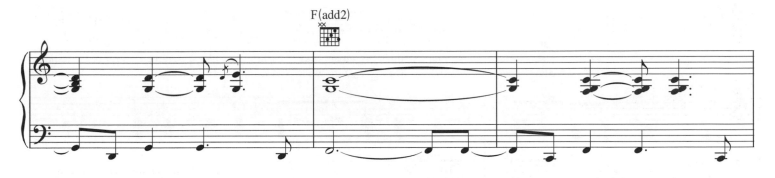

Now that _____ she's back _____ in the at-
_____ she's back _____ from that soul _____

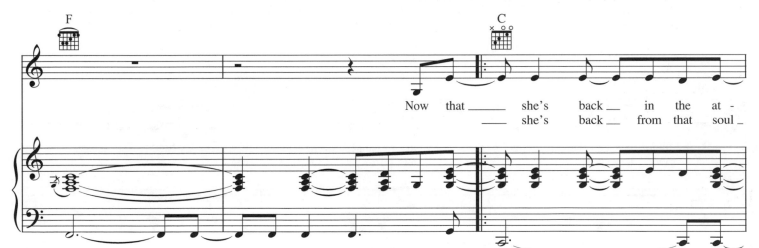

-mos - phere with drops _____ of Ju - pi - ter in _____ her hair _____ hey
- va - ca - tion, trac - ing her way _____ through the con - stel - la - tion,

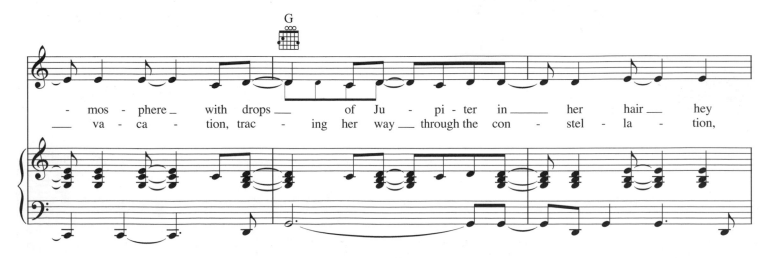

hey, _____
hey _____ hey. _____

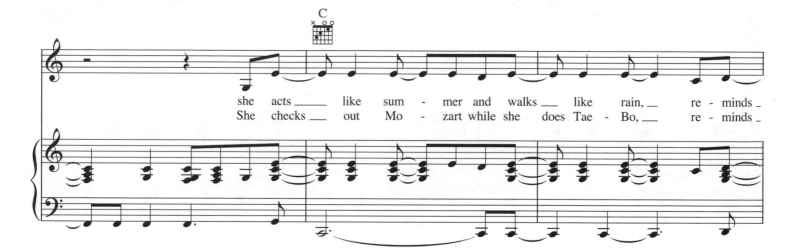

she acts ____ like sum - mer and walks ____ like rain, ____ re - minds ____
She checks ____ out Mo - zart while she does Tae - Bo, ____ re - minds ____

____ me that ____ there's a time to change, hey hey. _____
____ me that ____ there's ____ room to grow, ____ hey hey. _____

Since ____
Now that ____

54

the re-turn from her stay on the moon, she lis-tens like spring and she talks
she's back in the at-mos-phere I'm a-fraid that she might think

like June. Hey hey hey
of me as plain old Jane, told a sto-ry 'bout a man who was

hey. hey
too a-fraid to fly so he nev-er did land. (1.,D.S.) But tell me, did you
(2.) But tell me, did the

sail a-cross the sun? Did you make it to the Milk-y Way
wind sweep you off your feet? Did you fin-'lly get the chance to dance

to see ____ that lights ____ all fad - ed ____ and that heav - en is o -
a - long ____ the light ____ of day, _____ and head back to the

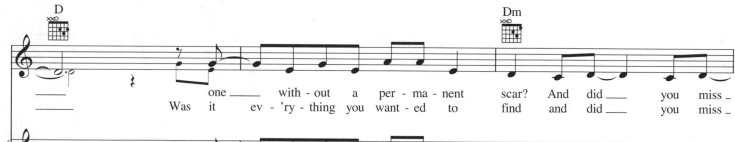

- ver - rat - ed? ____ And tell me, did you fall for a shoot - ing star, ____
Milk - y Way? And tell me, did Ve - nus blow ____ your mind? ____

one ____ with - out a per - ma - nent scar? And did ____ you miss ____
Was it ev - 'ry - thing you want - ed to find and did ____ you miss ____

To Coda ⊕

me ____ while ____ you were look - ing for ____ your - self ____ out there? ____
me ____ while ____ you were look - ing for ____ your - self ____ out there? ____

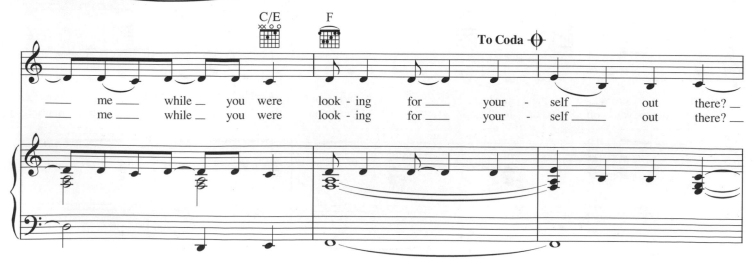

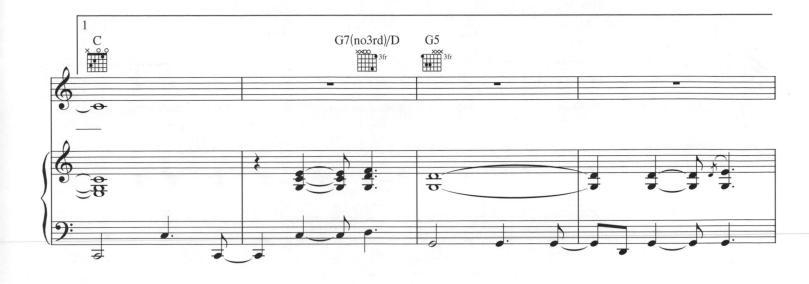

Now that _

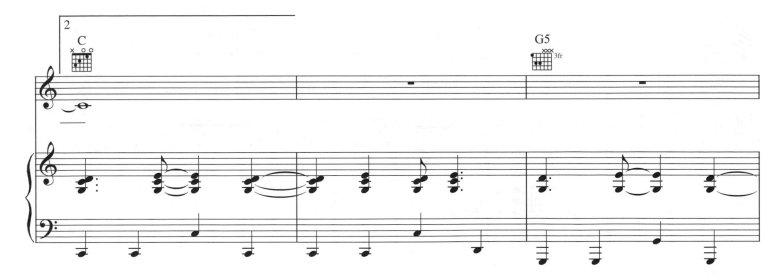

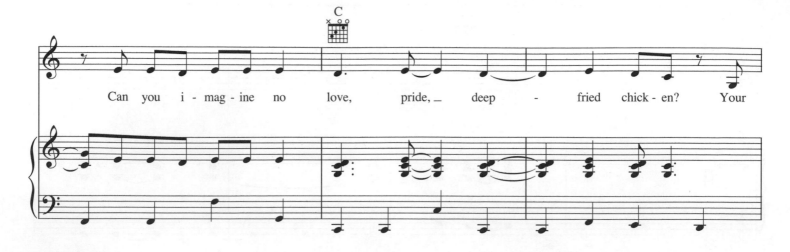

Can you i-mag-ine no love, pride, __ deep - fried chick-en? Your

best friend __ al - ways stick-ing up for you, ___

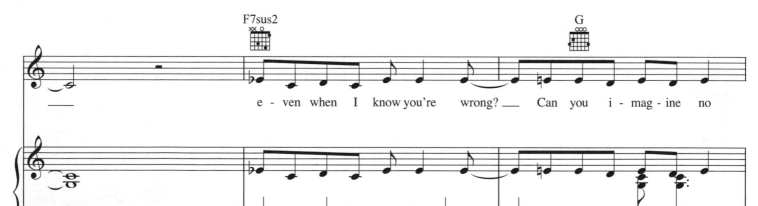

___ e - ven when I know you're wrong? __ Can you i-mag-ine no

first dance? _ Freeze - dried Ro - mance? Five - hour __ phone

58

con - ver - sa - tion? The best soy lat - te that you ev - er had ___ and

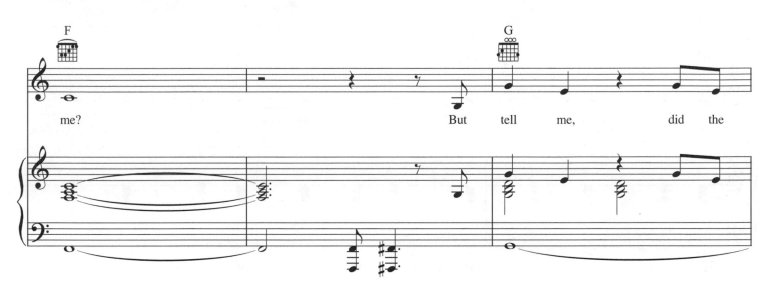

me? But tell me, did the

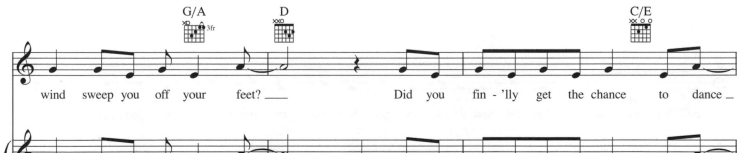

wind sweep you off your feet? ___ Did you fin -'lly get the chance to dance ___

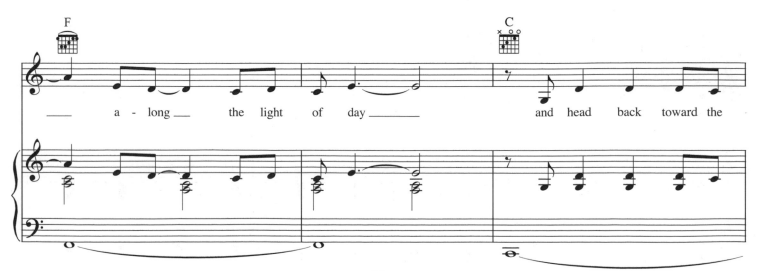

___ a - long ___ the light of day _____ and head back toward the

D.S. al Coda

Milk - y Way? _ And

CODA

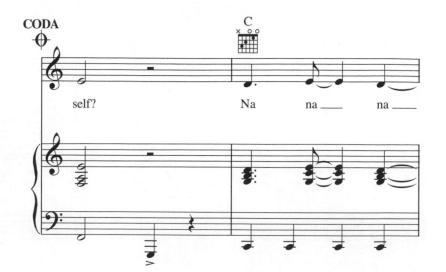

self? Na na _ na _

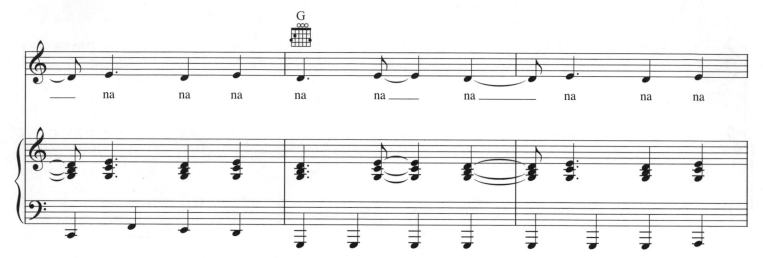

_ na na na na na _ na _ na na na

na na na na. _ And did you fin - 'lly get the chance to dance _ a - long _ the light

of day? _ Na na _ na _ na na na

na   na___   na_____   na   na   na   na na na na.____   from a
And did you fall

shoot - ing   star,_____   fall   from a   shoot - ing   star?_____

Na   na___   na_____   na   na   na   na   na___   na_____

___   na   na na.   And are you lone - ly___ look - ing for your - self___ out   there?

rall.

GOOD SOULS

Words & Music by James Walsh, James Stelfox,
Barry Westhead & Benjamin Byrne

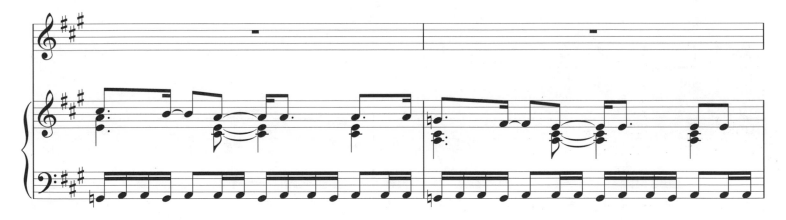

One good day of the week_____ and I'll_____ be

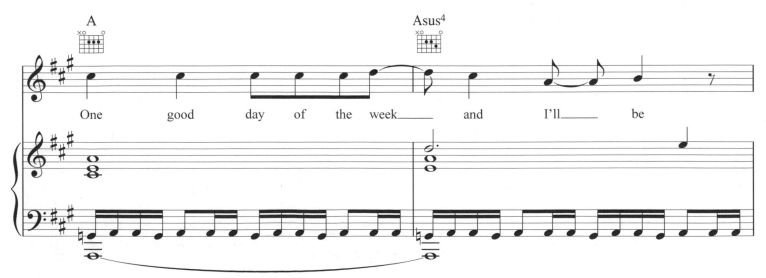

66

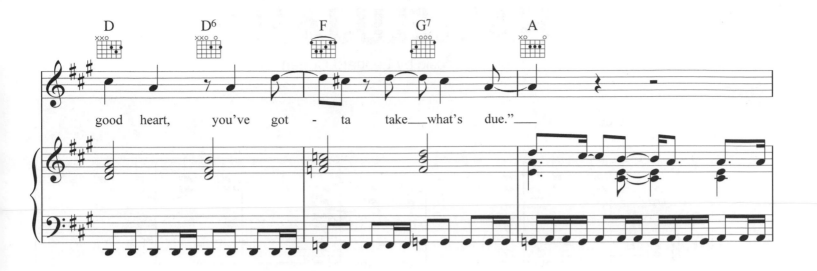

good heart, you've got - ta take____what's due."____

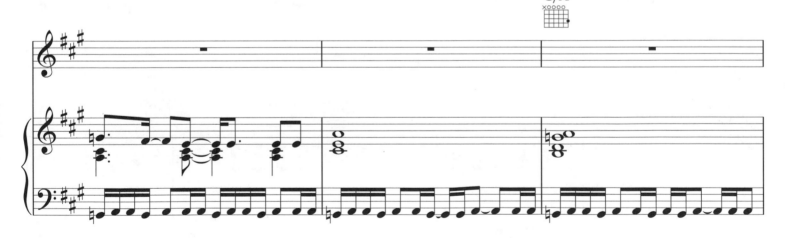

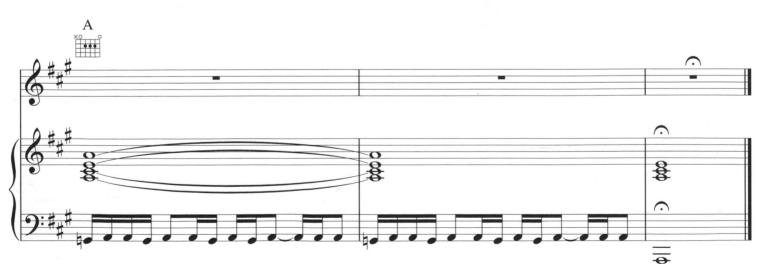

HALLELUJAH

Words & Music by Leonard Cohen

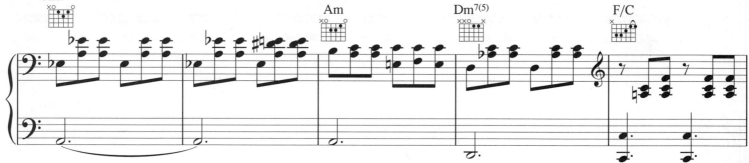

1. Well, I heard there was a se-cret chord that Da - vid played and it
(2.) faith was strong but you need-ed proof. You saw her bath - ing___
(3.) ba - by, I've been here be - fore, I've seen this room and I've
(4.) was a time whenyou let me know what's real - ly go - ing

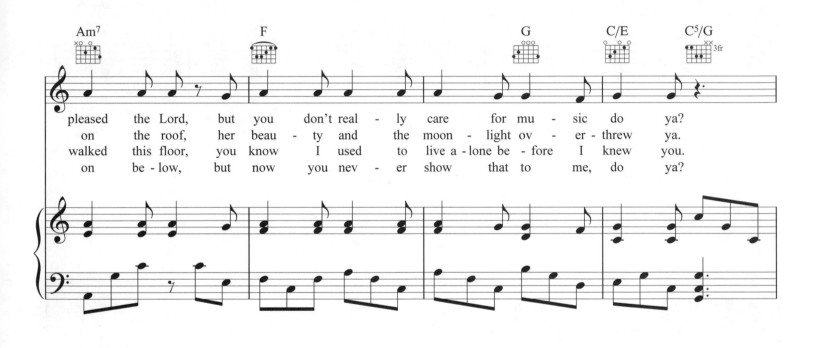

pleased the Lord, but you don't real - ly care for mu - sic do ya?
on the roof, her beau - ty and the moon - light ov - er - threw ya.
walked this floor, you know I used to live a - lone be - fore I knew you.
on be - low, but now you nev - er show that to me, do ya?

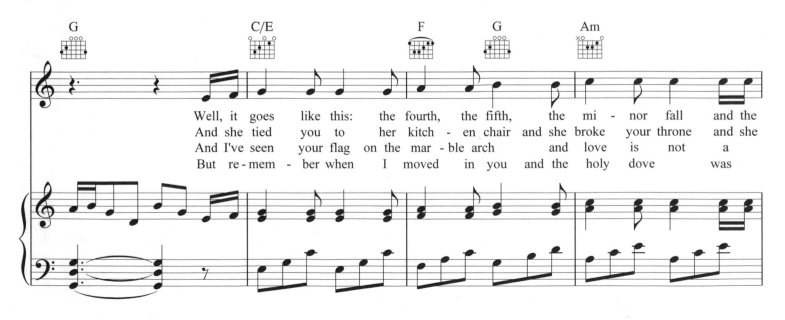

Well, it goes like this: the fourth, the fifth, the mi - nor fall and the
And she tied you to her kitch - en chair and she broke your throne and she
And I've seen your flag on the mar - ble arch and love is not a
But re - mem - ber when I moved in you and the holy dove was

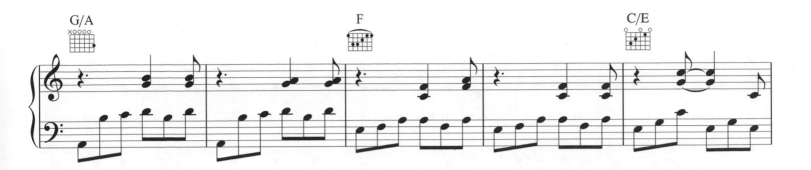

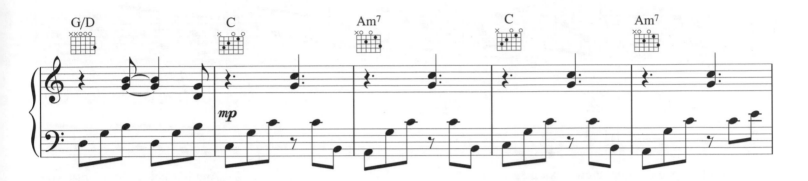

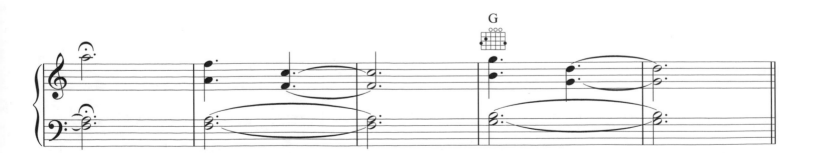

May-be there's a God a-bove, but all I've ev-er learned from love was how to shoot some-

-bo-dy who out-drew ya.___ And it's not a cry that you

hear at night, it's not some-bo-dy who's seen the light, it's a cold and it's a bro-ken Hal-le-

-lu - jah.___ Hal-le-lu - jah, Hal-le-lu - jah.

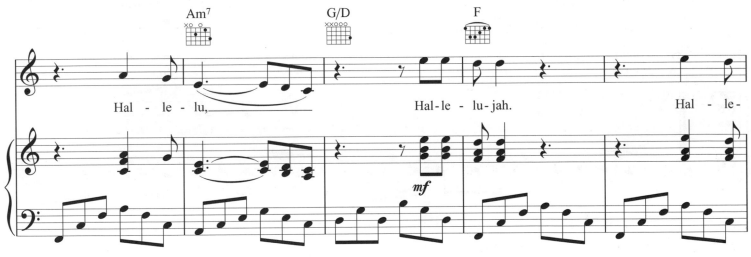

73

HEARTBEATS

Words & Music by Olof Bjorn Dreijer & Andersson Dreijer

1. One night to be con - fused, one night to speed up truth;
2. One night of mag - ic rush; the start, a sim - ple touch.

we had a prom - ise made, four hands and then a - way.
One night to push and scream, and then re - lief.

you knew the hand of the de-vil.____

And you____ kept us a-wake with

wolf's teeth; shar-ing diff-'rent heart-beats in one night.__

D.S. al Coda　　　　⊕ **Coda**

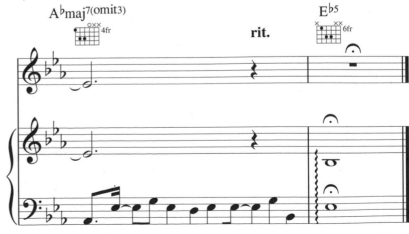

HOW TO SAVE A LIFE

Words & Music by Joseph King & Isaac Slade

I lost_____ a friend some-where__ a - long__ in the bit-ter-ness. And

I would have_ stayed up__ with you_ all night, had I__ known

how to save___ a life.__

'ry - thing,___ or he'll say___ he's just not___ the same,___ and

you'll be - gin___ to won - der why___ you came. Where did I___ go wrong?___

___ I lost___ a friend some - where___ a - long___ in the bit - ter - ness. And

I would have___ stayed up___ with you___ all night, had I___ known

how to save____ a life. how to save____ a life.____

How to save____ a life,____

how to save____ a life.

Where did I____ go wrong?____ I lost____ a friend some - where____ a - long____

in the bit-ter-ness. And I would have stayed up with you all night,

had I known how to save a life. how to save a life.

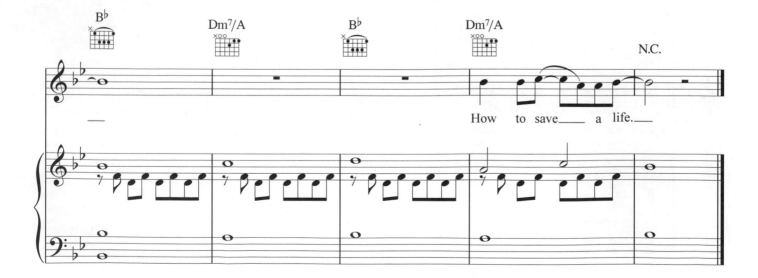

How to save a life.

HOW YOU REMIND ME

Words & Music by Chad Kroeger, Michael Kroeger, Ryan Peake & Ryan Vikedal

Drop D tuning: ⑥ = D

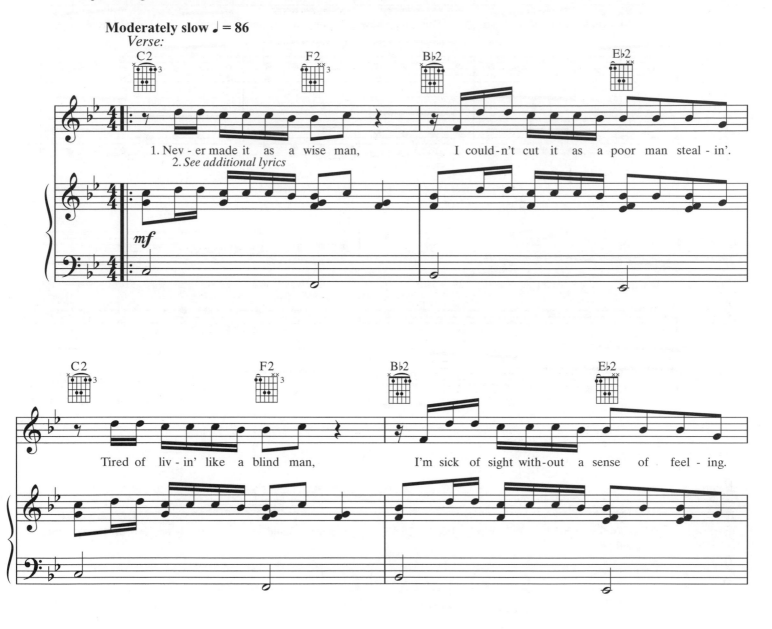

Chorus:

86

To Coda ⊕

These five words___ in my head   scream, "Are we hav - in' fun___ yet?"___

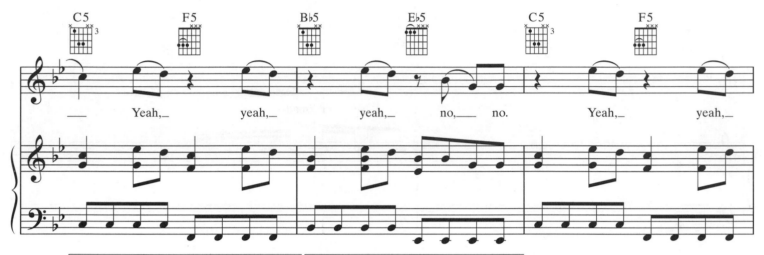

___ Yeah,___   yeah,___   yeah,___   no,___ no.   Yeah,___   yeah,___

1.   2.

yeah,___   no,___ no.   yeah,___   no,___ no.   Yeah,___   yeah,___

yeah,___   no,___ no.   Yeah,___   yeah,___   yeah,___   no,___ no.

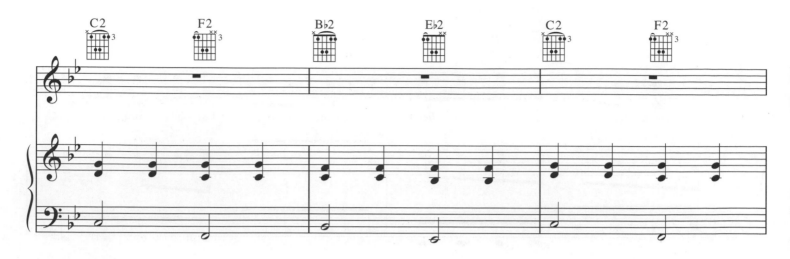

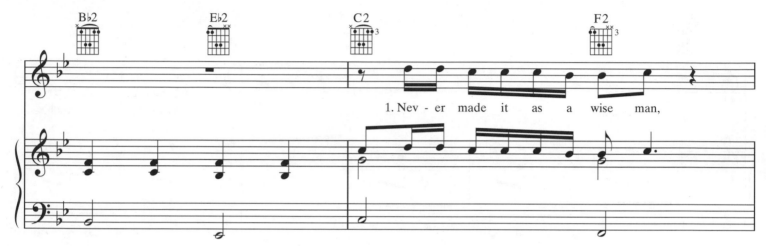

1. Nev - er made it as a wise man,

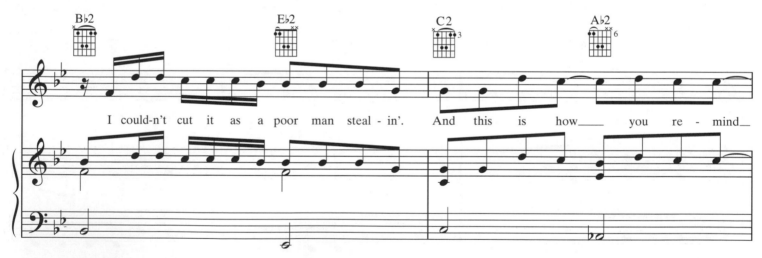

I could-n't cut it as a poor man steal - in'. And this is how___ you re - mind___

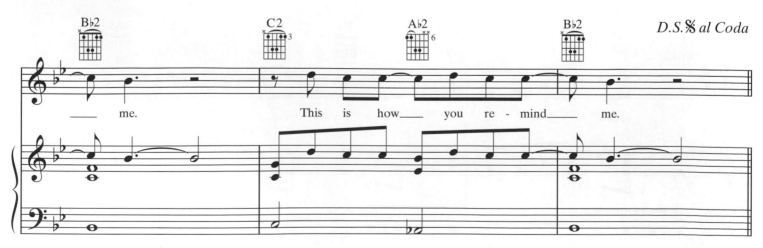

___ me. This is how___ you re - mind___ me.

D.S.%al Coda

Coda

Yeah,___ yeah,___ are we hav-in' fun___ yet?

Yeah,___ yeah,___ are we hav-in' fun___ yet?

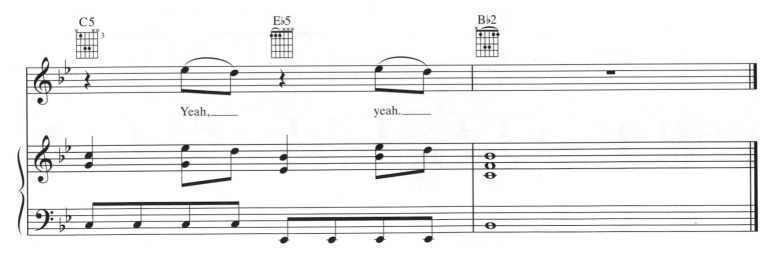

Yeah,___ yeah.___

Verse 2:
It's not like you didn't know that.
I said I love you and swear I still do.
And it must have been so bad.
'Cause livin' with me must have damn near killed you.
This is how you remind me of what I really am.
This is how you remind me of what I really am.
(To Chorus:)

IN THE MORNING

Words & Music by James Skelly

Shut the bed-room win-dow in the morn-ing,
Thought I was sleep-ing: it was just a dream,
When I leave I try not to wake her,
She wrote my name on a red tel-e-phone box,

go to the shop, make plans to be leav-ing...
an al-ley cat chewing on dead leaves...
tea and a toast to yes-ter-day's ca-pers...
when I got there she'd al-read-y rubbed it off...

In the morn - ing.

Out of the dark____ and in-to the light,____ when the morn-ing comes

I will be al - right.____

D.S. al Coda (with repeat)

To Coda ⊕

IRONIC

Words by Alanis Morissette
Music by Alanis Morissette & Glen Ballard

Original key: E major

ev -'ry-thing blows_ up in___ your face.___   3. A

Coda

beau- ti- ful hus- band._ And is-n't it i - ron- ic... don't you___

think? A lit-tle too___ i - ron-ic and yeah, I real-ly do think... it's like rain___

___ on your wed ding__ day. It's a free_ ride___ when you're al - read-y paid. It's the good ad-vice

that you just did - n't take.__ And who would have thought,_ it fi - gures.

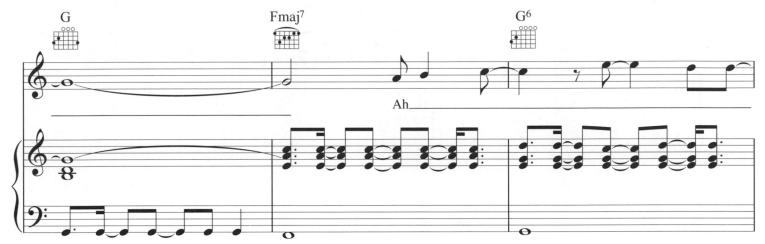

Ah_____

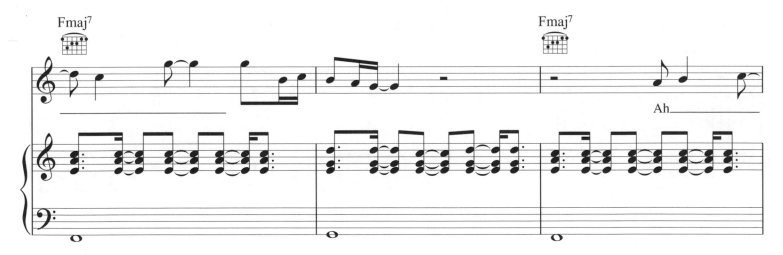

Ah_____

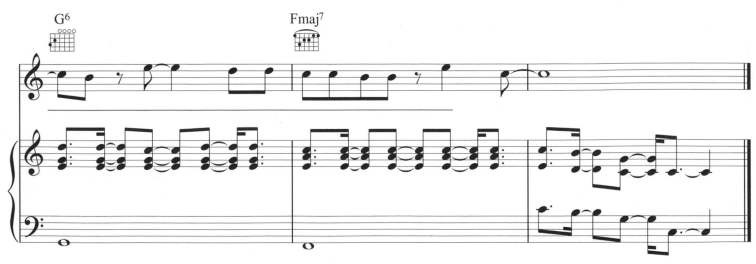

Journey From A To B

Words & Music by Damon Gough

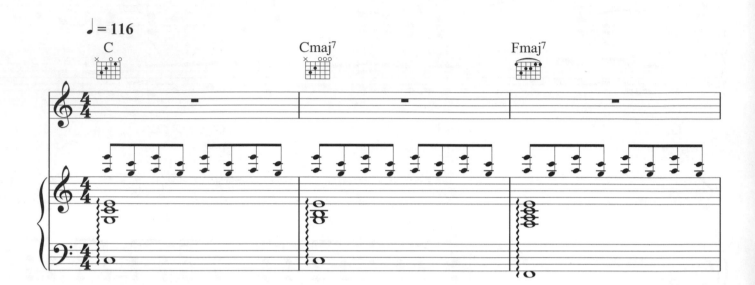

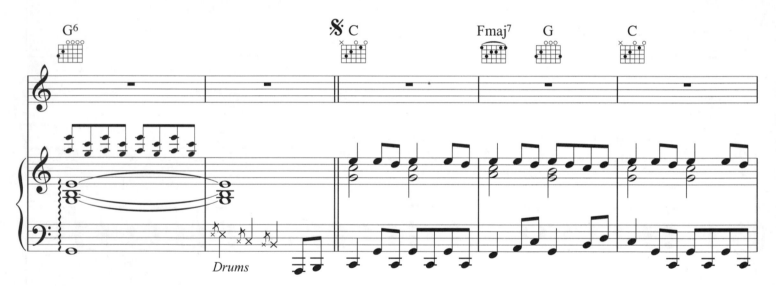

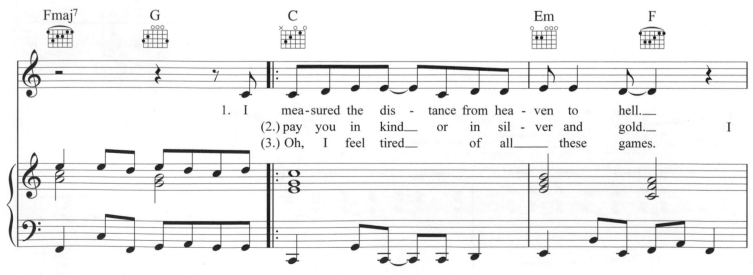

1. I mea-sured the dis-tance from hea-ven to hell.__
(2.) pay you in kind__ or in sil-ver and gold.__ I
(3.) Oh, I feel tired__ of all__ these games.

Lullaby

Words & Music by Shawn Mullins

(spoken) 1. She grew up with the child-ren of the stars

in the Hol-ly-wood Hills and the Bou-le-vard._____

Her par-ents threw big par-ties, ev-'ry-one was there,_____

they hung out with folks like Den-nis Hop-per 'n' Bob See-ger 'n' Son-ny and Cher.

But she feels safe now in this bar on Fair-fax.
(2.) And all her friends tell her she's so pret-ty,

And from the stage I can tell that she can't let go and she can't re-lax.
but she'd be a whole lot prettier if she smiled once in a while.

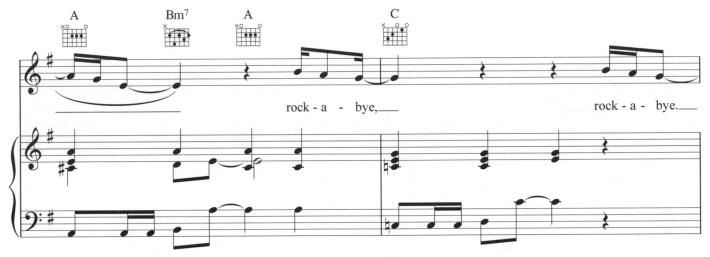

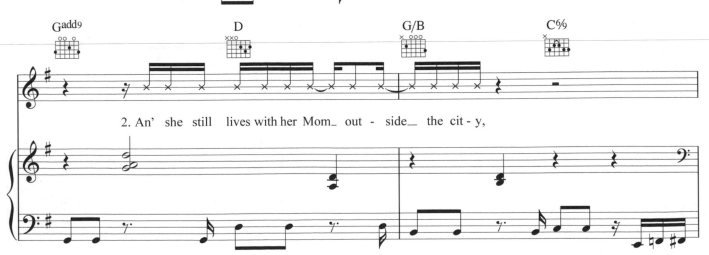

down that street a-bout a half-a-mile.

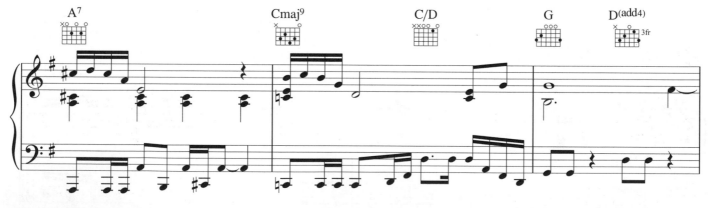

3. I told her, I ain't so sure a-bout this___ place.

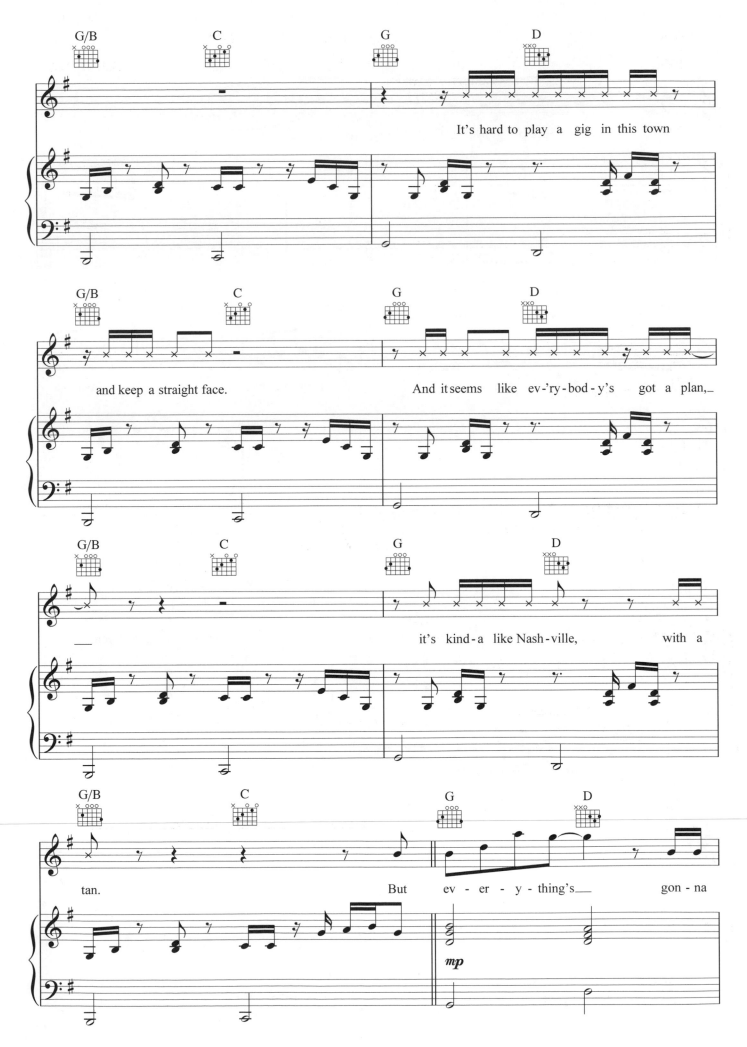

It's hard to play a gig in this town

and keep a straight face.   And it seems like ev-'ry-bod-y's got a plan,__

__   it's kind-a like Nash-ville,   with a

tan.   But ev-er-y-thing's__   gon-na

Ev - er - y - thing's_____ gon - na

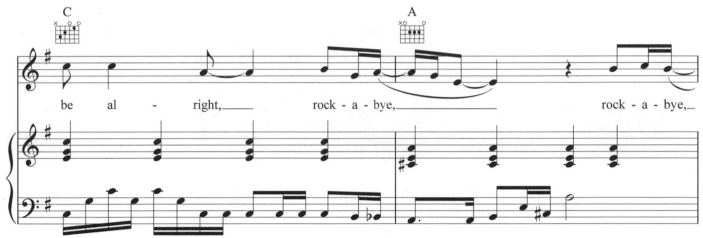

be al - right,_____ rock - a - bye,_____ rock - a - bye,_____

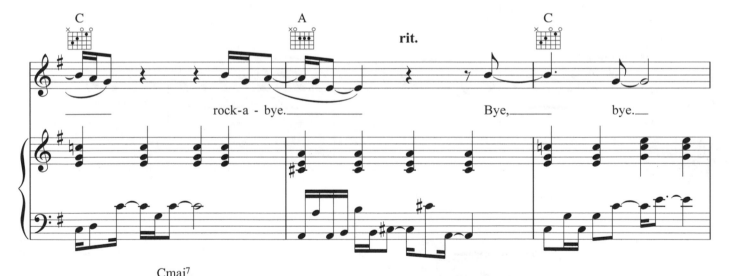

rock-a - bye._____ Bye,_____ bye._____

Bye,_____ bye.

111

NATURE'S LAW

Words & Music by Danny McNamara, Richard McNamara,
Martin Glover, Mike Heaton, Steven Firth & Michael Dale

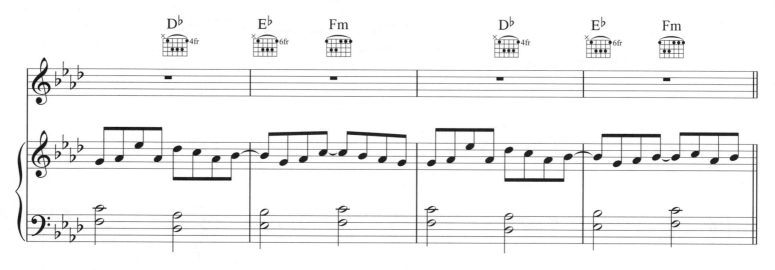

1. I tried to fight the feel-ing, the feel-ing took me down. I strug-gled and I
2. I'll live with nev-er know-ing if know-ing's gon-na change. I'll stop the feel-ing

You should nev - er fight___ your feel - ings_____ when your ve - ry bones___

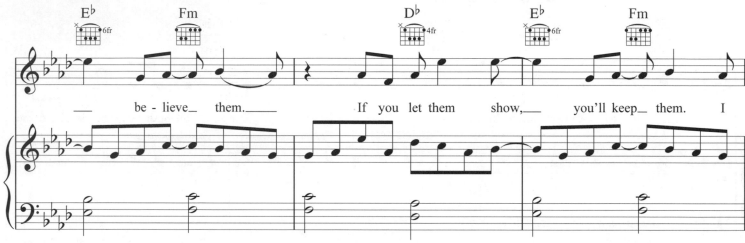

___ be - lieve_ them.____ If you let them show,___ you'll keep_ them. I

know_ you've hurt_ but soon___ you'll rise___ a - gain.___ A - gain,___ a - gain,

___ a - gain,____ a - gain,____ a - gain,____ a - gain,___ a - gain._

You should nev - er fight___ your feel - ings___ when your ve - ry bones___ ___ be - lieve___ them.___ You should nev - er fight___ your feel - ings. You have___ to fol - low na - ture's law.___

rit.

NAÏVE

Words & Music by Luke Pritchard, Hugh Harris,
Max Rafferty & Paul Garred

1. I'm not say - ing it___ was your
2. I may say___ it___ was your

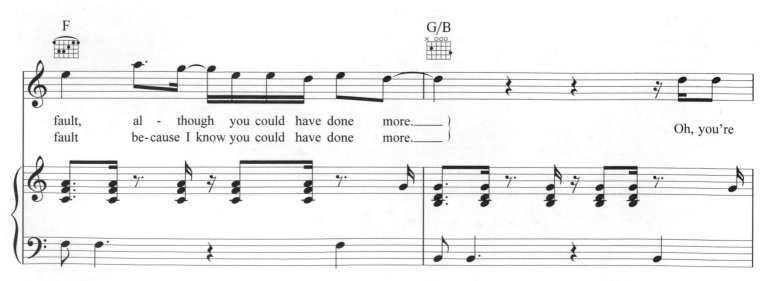

fault,   al - though you could have done   more.___
fault   be - cause I know you could have done   more.___

Oh, you're

so na - ive yet so... How could this be done by such a smil - ing sweet - heart?

Oh, and your sweet and pret - ty face, it's such an ug - ly word

for some - thing so beau - ti - ful. Oh, that ev - 'ry time I look in - side you're on his side.

I know she knows that I'm not fond of ask - ing. True or false it may be,

-ter's edge, the moon is low_ to-night._

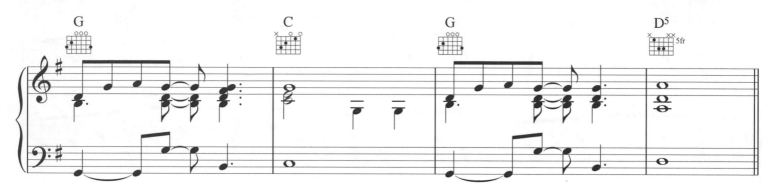

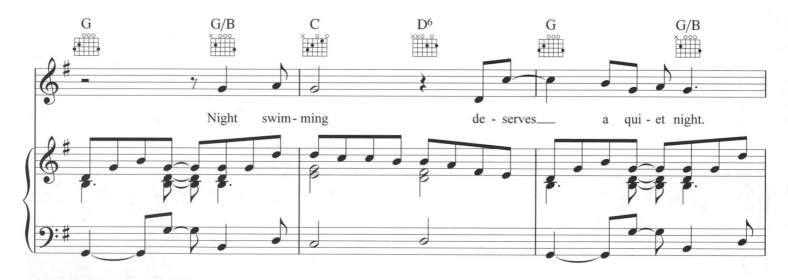

Night swim-ming de-serves_ a qui-et night.

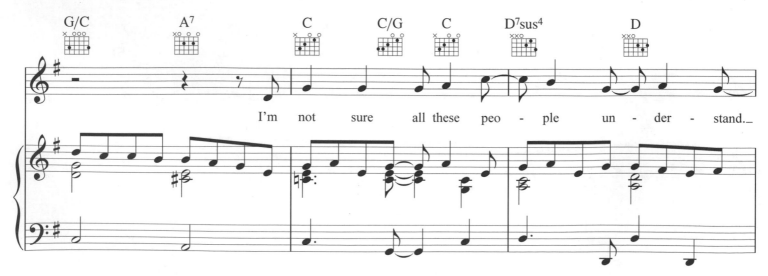

I'm not sure all these peo-ple un-der-stand._

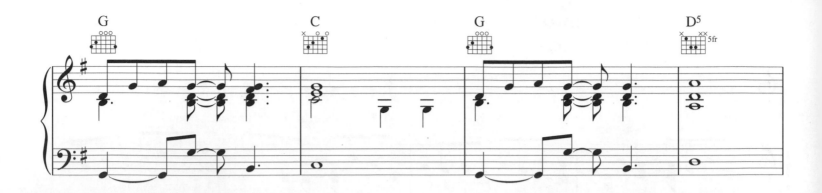

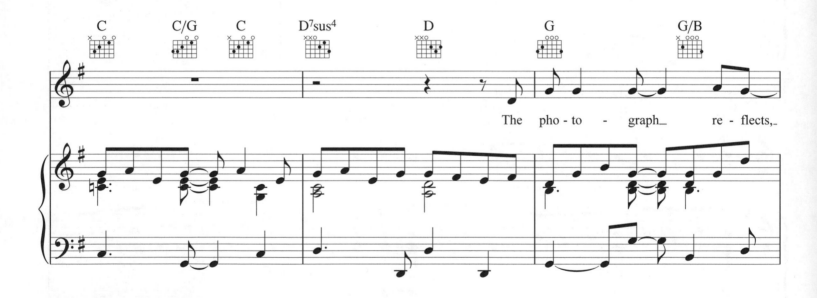

The pho-to-graph__ re - flects,__

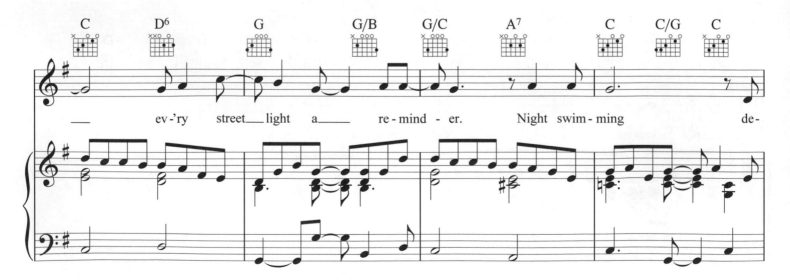

__ ev-'ry street__ light a____ re - mind - er. Night swim - ming de-

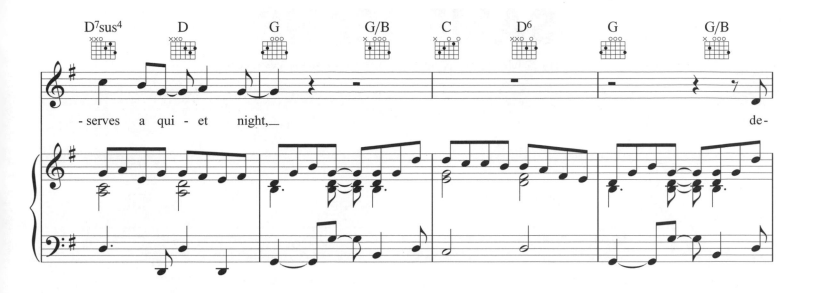

-serves a qui - et night,___ de-

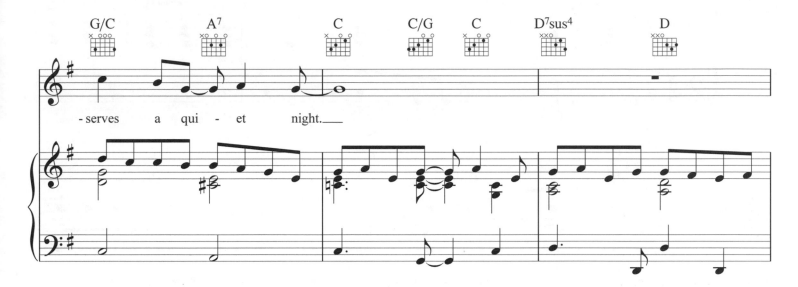

-serves a qui - et night.___

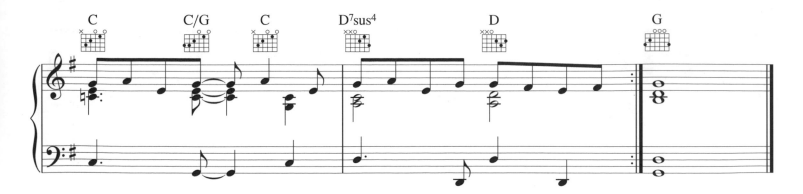

Same Jeans

Words & Music by Kyle Falconer & Keiren Webster

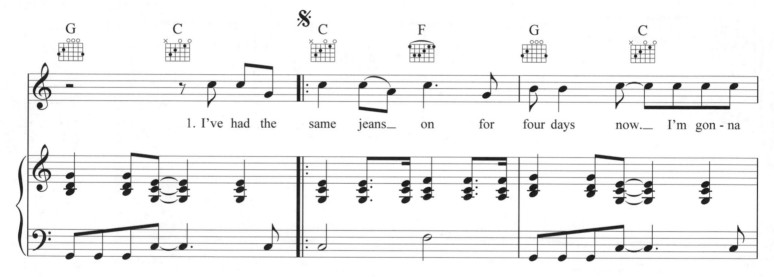

1. I've had the same jeans on for four days now. I'm gon-na

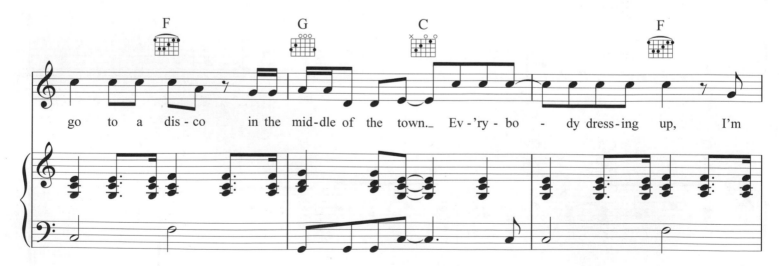

go to a dis-co in the mid-dle of the town. Ev-'ry-bo - dy dress-ing up, I'm

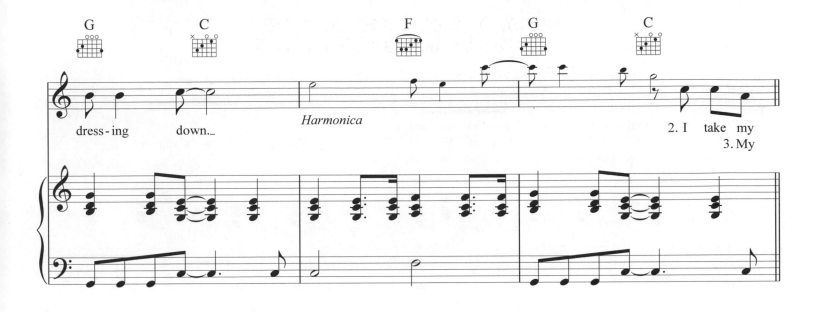

dress-ing down._

Harmonica

2. I take my
3. My

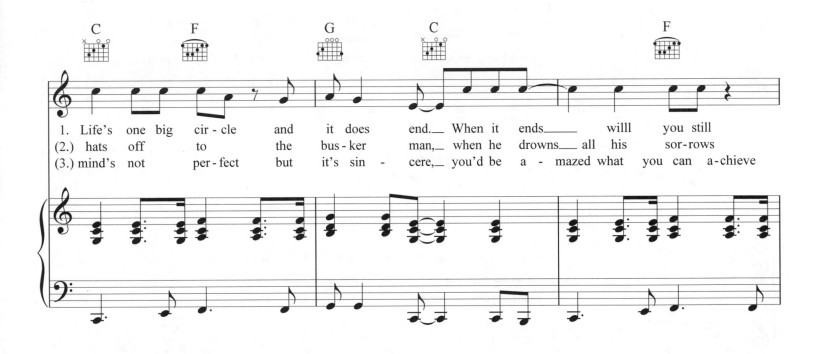

1. Life's one big cir-cle and it does end._ When it ends____ willl you still
(2.) hats off to the bus-ker man,_ when he drowns___ all his sor-rows
(3.) mind's not per-fect but it's sin - cere,_ you'd be a - mazed what you can a-chieve

be my friend?_ I'm not mak-ing a fool of my-self._ Oh, tell me
sing-ing songs._ Not ev-'ry-thing has worked out to plan,_ but be-lieve
in the end._ And you try_____ so hard but you're all____ gon - na quit._ And I know

138

feet back on the ground.

Guitar

feet back on the ground. So! When you look in the mir-ror.

I've had the

Re - flect-ing back at you some-one that you don't know.

Lyrics: That's just made your head spin a - round._ So get your - self to - geth - er and get your feet back on_ the ground._

Same jeans on for four_ days now. Ev - 'ry - bo - dy's dress - ing up, I'm dress - ing down.

I'm not mak-ing a fool of my-self.___ Now be-lieve me la-dy, I___ can tell.___

Same jeans on for four___ days now. Ev-'ry-bo-dy's dress-ing up, I'm dress-ing down.

I'm not mak-ing a fool of my-self.___ Now be-lieve me la-dy, I___ can tell.___

Put Your Records On

Words & Music by John Beck, Steven Chrisanthou & Corinne Bailey Rae

Girl, put your re - cords on, tell me your fav - 'rite song.

You go a - head, let your hair down. Sap - phire and fad - ed jeans,

I hope you get your dreams. Just go a - head; let your hair down.

1.

You're gon - na find your - self some - where, some - how.

SMILE

Words & Music by Jackie Mittoo, Clement Dodd,
Iyiola Babalola, Darren Lewis & Lily Allen

When you first left me,___ I did-n't know what to say.___ I'd nev-er been on my
could-n't stop laugh-ing;___ no, I just could-n't help my-self. See, you messed up my

own that way; just sat by my-self all day.
men-tal health; I was quite un - well.___

I was so lost back then, but, with a lit-tle help___ from my friends,

I found the light in the tun-nel at the end.___

150

At first,_____ when I see you cry,_____ it makes me

smile,_____ yeah, it makes me smile._____

At worst,_____ I feel bad for a while,_____ but then I just

1.
smile;____ I go a-head and smile.____

2.
smile.____

151

SOMEWHERE ONLY WE KNOW

Words & Music by Tim Rice-Oxley,
Tom Chaplin & Richard Hughes

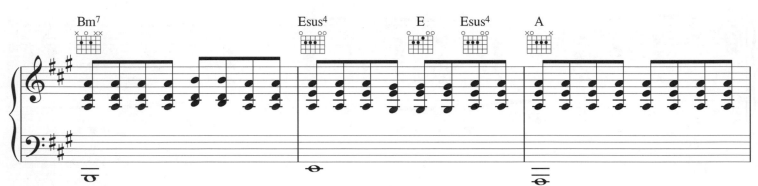

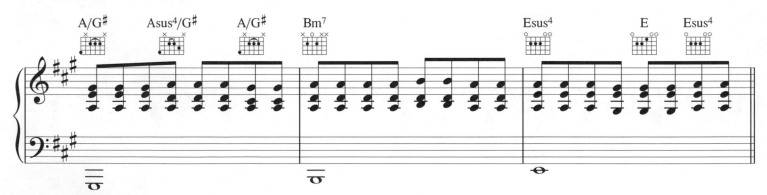

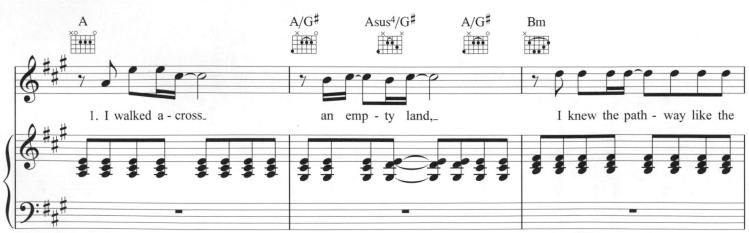

1. I walked a-cross an emp-ty land, I knew the path-way like the

154

155

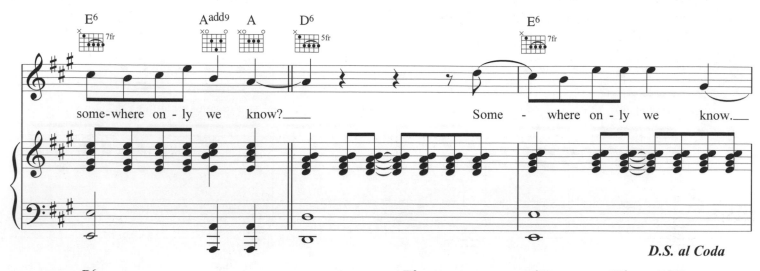

some-where on - ly we know?____ Some - where on - ly we know.____

D.S. al Coda

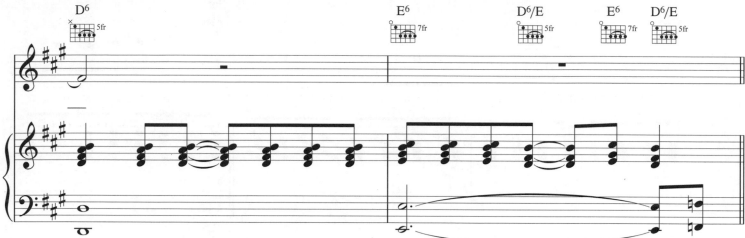

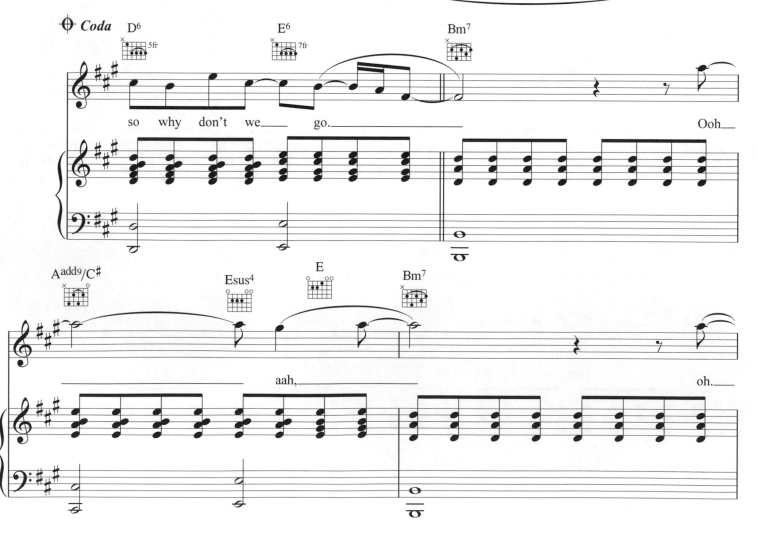

so why don't we____ go._____ Ooh____

aah,_____ oh.____

156

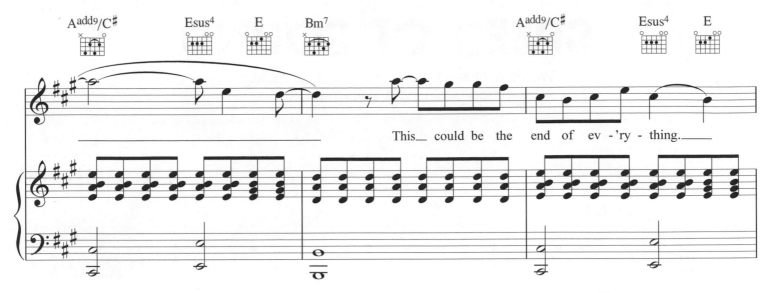

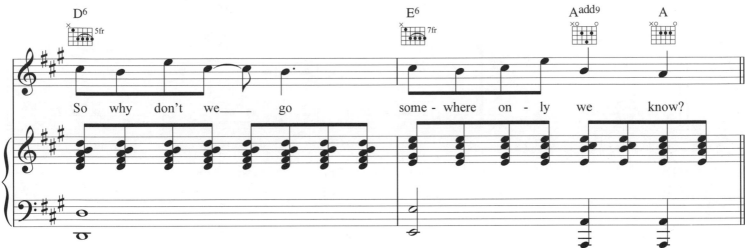

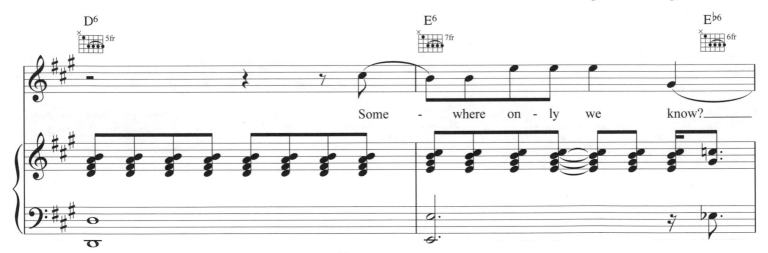

Speed of Sound

Words & Music by Guy Berryman, Chris Martin,
Jon Buckland & Will Champion

1. How long be - fore I get in,_____ be - fore it_____
2. Look up, I look up at night,___ plan - ets are mov -
3. I - deas that you'll nev - er find,___ all the in - ven -

All those signs,___ I knew what they meant, some things you can't in-vent. Some get made___ ___ and some___ get sent.___ Ooh.___ And

SOPHIA

Words & Music by Nerina Pallot

166

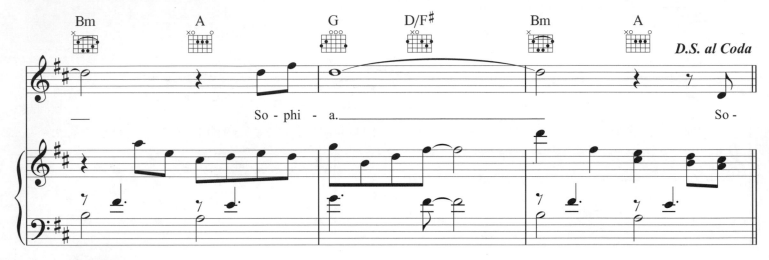

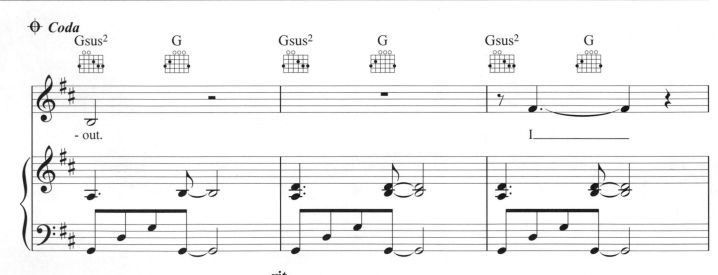

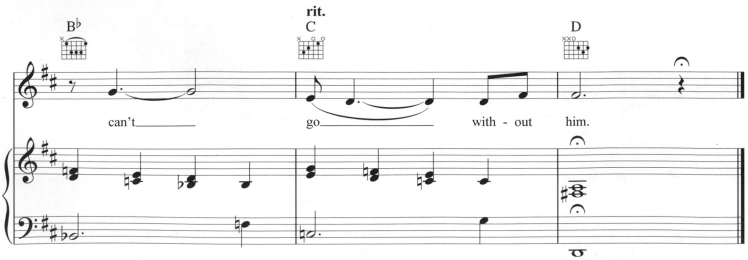

SUDDENLY I SEE

Words & Music by KT Tunstall

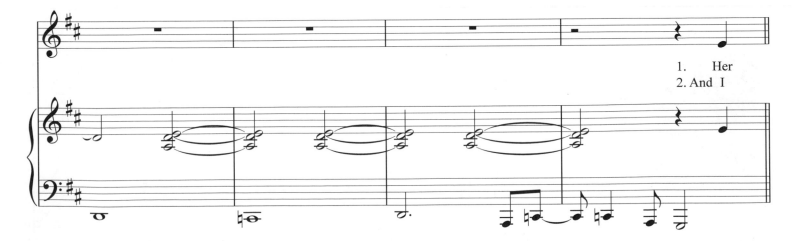

see

why the hell___ it means___ so much___ to me.

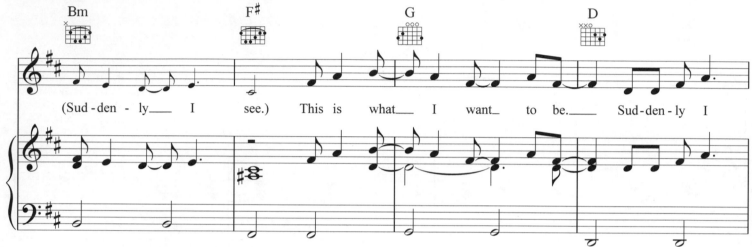

(Sud-den-ly___ I see.) This is what___ I want___ to be.___ Sud-den-ly I

see

why the hell___ it means___ so much___ to me.___

___ And she's tall-er than most

and she's look-ing at me.

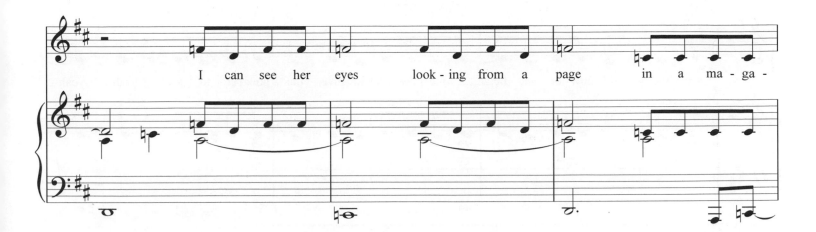

I can see her eyes look-ing from a page in a ma-ga-

-zine. She makes___ me feel___ like I could be a

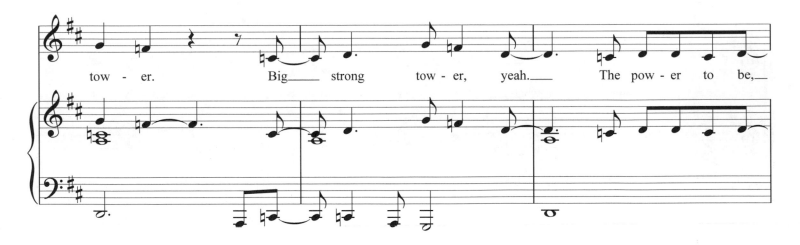

tow - er. Big___ strong tow - er, yeah.___ The pow - er to be,___

___ the pow - er to give, the pow - er to see,___ yeah, yeah.___ (Sud - den - ly I

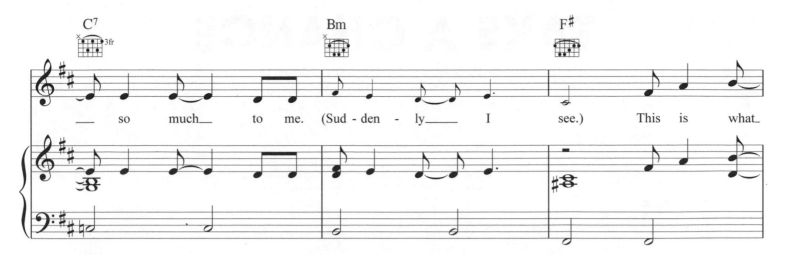

— so much _to me. (Sud - den - ly_ _I_ _see.)_ _This is what_

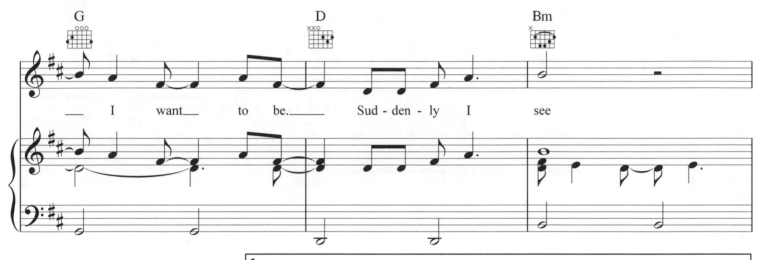

— I want _to be._ _Sud - den - ly_ _I_ _see_

1.

Repeat ad lib.

why _the hell_ _it means_ _so much_ _to me._

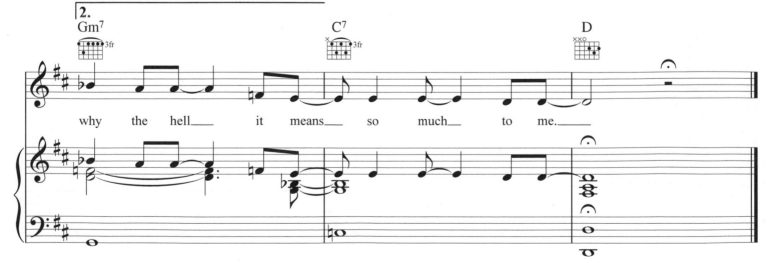

2.

why _the hell_ _it means_ _so much_ _to me._

TAKE A CHANCE

Words & Music by Romeo Stodart

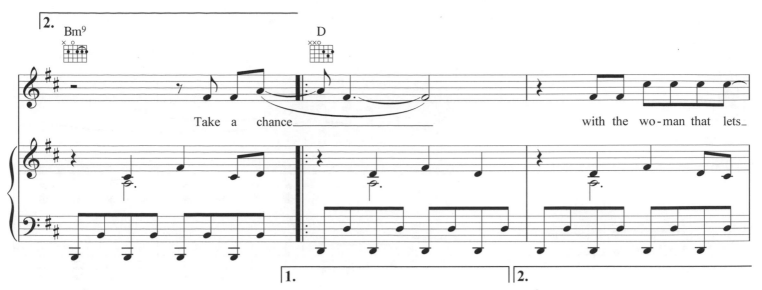

Take a chance_____ with the wo-man that lets_

___ you. Take a chance___ 2. How

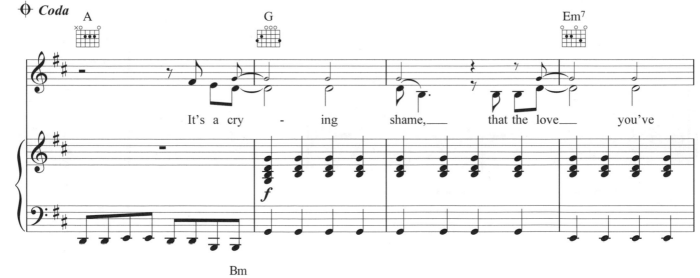

It's a cry - ing shame,___ that the love___ you've

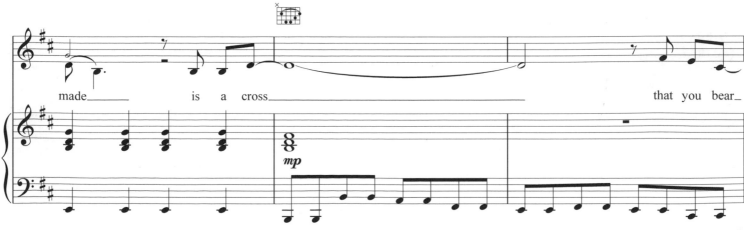

made_____ is a cross_____ that you bear_

180

THEY CAN'T BUY THE SUNSHINE

Words & Music by Olly Knights & Gale Paridjanian

Original key Db major.

♩ = 120

1. All in all it's been a blast but fame and for - tune
2. We may have sold our ve - ry souls, the ghost's in - side the

nev - er lasts. So we'll take re - fuge___ in the sound.. They
ra - di - o. They warned us once and they___ told us twice,___

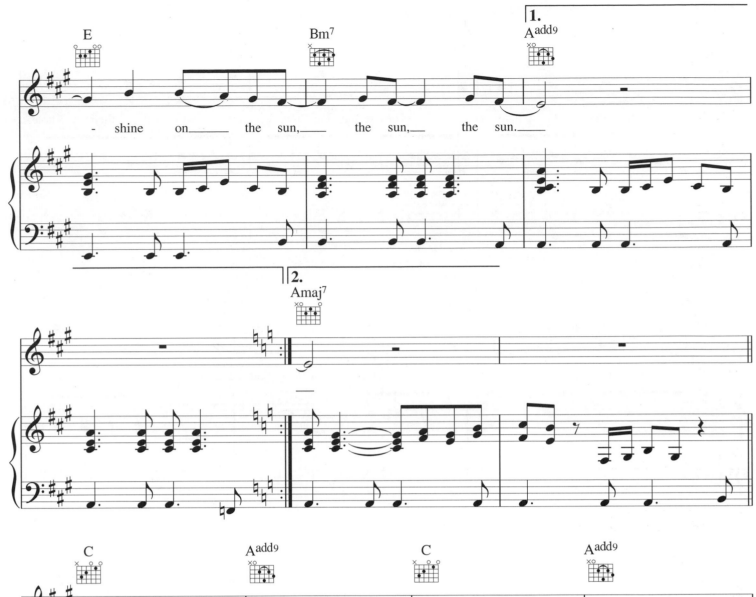

The cred-it card sky-line ris-es high,___ crush-ing the sky_

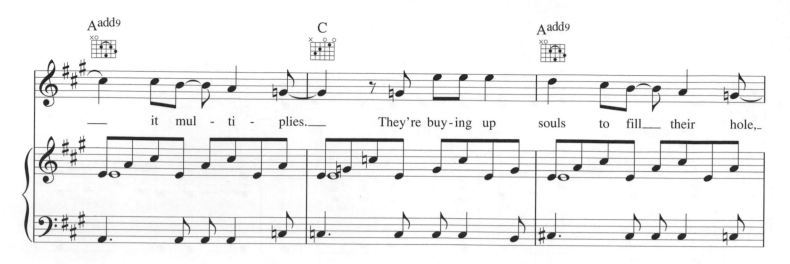

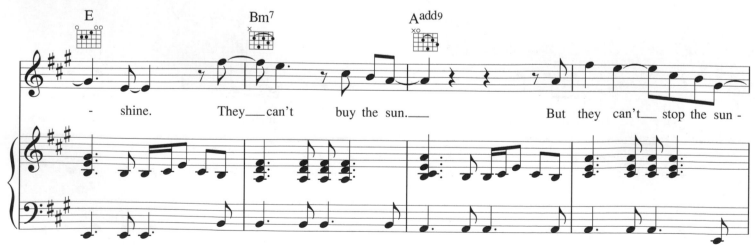

- shine._ They_can't stop the sun - shine._ They_can't stop the sun-

- shine on___ the sun,__ the sun,_ the sun.__ Shine.

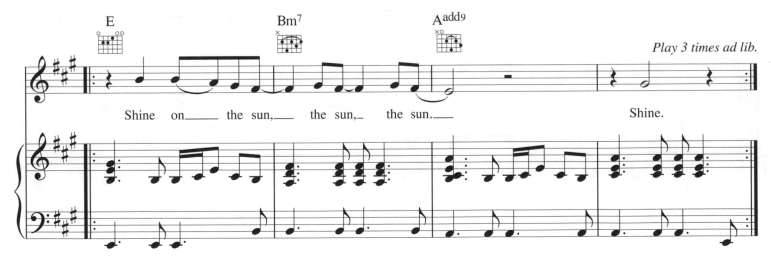

Play 3 times ad lib.

Shine on___ the sun,__ the sun,_ the sun.__ Shine.

Shine on___ the sun,__ the sun,_ the sun.__

VALERIE

Words & Music by Sean Payne, David McCabe,
Abi Harding, Boyan Chowdhury & Russel Pritchard

think of all the things what you're doin', and in my head I make a pic-

-ture. 'Cause since I've come on home, well, my bod-

(drum fill)

-y's been a mess. And I've missed your gin-ger hair and the way you like to dress.

Won't you come on o-ver, stop mak-ing a fool out of me.

Why — won't you come on o - ver Val - er - ie? _____ Val - er - ie. _

To Coda ⊕

_____ on up for sale, _ did you get a good law - yer?

2. Did you have _____ to go to jail, _ put your house _

_____ on up for sale, _ did you get a good law - yer?

I hope you did -n't catch a tan, _ I hope you

find the right man who'll fix it for____ ya.

Are you shop - pin' an - y - where,_ changed the

col - our of your hair,_ are you bus - y?

And did you have____ to pay_ the fine_ you were dodg -

-ing all the time,___ are you still diz - zy?

D.S. al Coda   𝄌 **Coda**

'Cause

(drum fill)

Val - er - ie,___

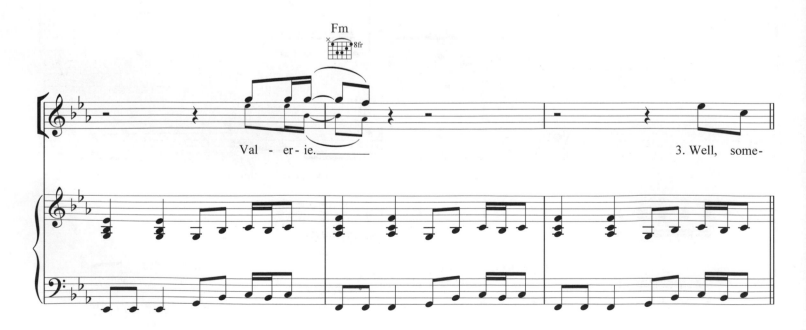

Val - er - ie.___   3. Well, some-

times I go out by my-self___ and I look___ a-cross___ the wa - ter.

Oo, oo.___   Oo, oo.___   Oo, oo.___

(clap)

(bass drum)

And I   think of all___ the things___   what you're doin',___   and in my head___ I make a pic-

Oo, oo.___   Oo, oo.___   Oo, oo.___

- ture.   'Cause

Oo, oo.___   Oo, oo.___

since I've come on home,___ well, my bod - y's been a mess.___ And I miss___

___ your gin - ger hair___ and the way___ you like to dress.___

Won't you come on o - ver, stop mak - ing a fool out of me.___

_____ Why___ won't you come on o - ver Val - er - ie?___

TUMBLE AND FALL

Words & Music by Grant Nicholas

1. All this for noth - ing   Yeah,_ yeah, yeah._____   Pray - ing and hop-
2. Hea - ven's a - bove___ us.   Yeah,_ yeah, yeah._____   Liv - ing in sol-

- ing,   fool - ing your - self...___   You know that you can___   give love a rea-
- ace,   I'd give you it all...___   Just for a day,___   just for a sec-

same___

since that day you went a - way___

I re - call,___

like the drops of sum-mer rain___

that fell___ on___ me.___

Come

back to me.___

Come back to me.___

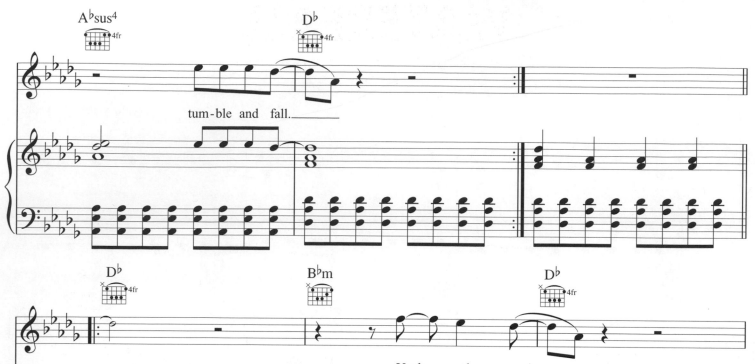

tum-ble and fall._____

Yeah,__ yeah, yeah._____

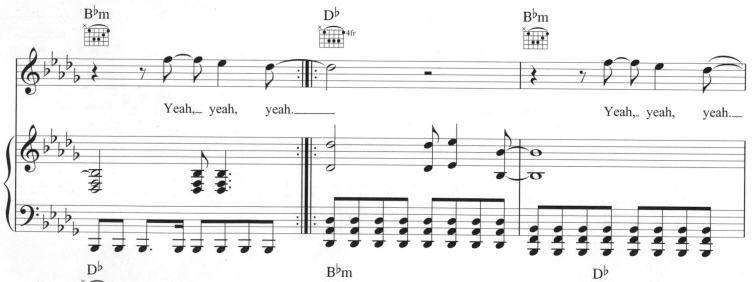

Yeah,__ yeah, yeah._____   Yeah,__ yeah, yeah.__

Yeah,__ yeah, yeah._____

WATERFALL

Words & Music by John Squire & Ian Brown

steal what she ne - ver could own, _____ and race from this hole she calls

home._____

2. Now_____ you're at the wheel._____ Tell me how,_____ how does it
4. See_____ the stee-ple pines._____ The hills_____ as old as

feel? So good to__ have e - qua-lised,_____ to
time. Soon to__ be put to__ the test,_____ to be

lift up__ the lids of__ your eyes._____
whipped by__ the winds of__ the west._____

3. As the miles_____ they dis - ap - pear._____ See
5. Stands_____ on shift - ing sands._____ The

land _____ be-gin_ to clear.
scales _____ held in her hands.

Free from_ the filth and_ the
The wind it_ just whips her_ and

scum, _____ this A - mer - i - can sat - el - lite's won. _____
wails, _____ and fills up_ her brig - an - tine sails. _____

She'll car - ry on through_ it all, she's a wa-ter-

She'll car - ry on through it all, she's a wa-ter-

- fall.

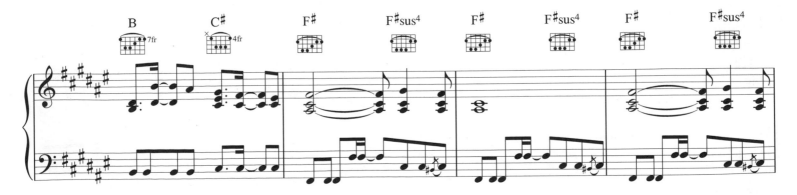

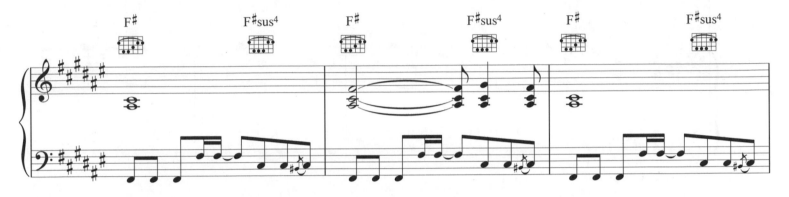

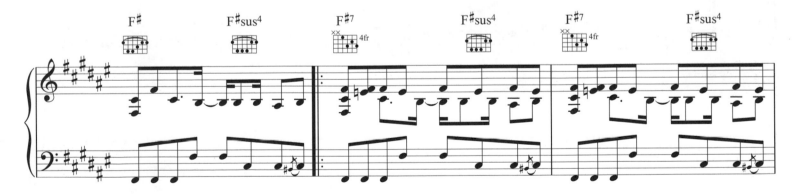

WHEREVER YOU WILL GO

Words & Music by Aaron Kamin & Alex Band

1. So late - ly, been won - d'rin, who will___ be there___ to take___ my place..
2. And may - be I'll find out a way___ to___ make it back___ some day..

___ When I'm___ gone, you'll need___ love to light___ the
___ To watch___ you, to guide___ you through___ the

209

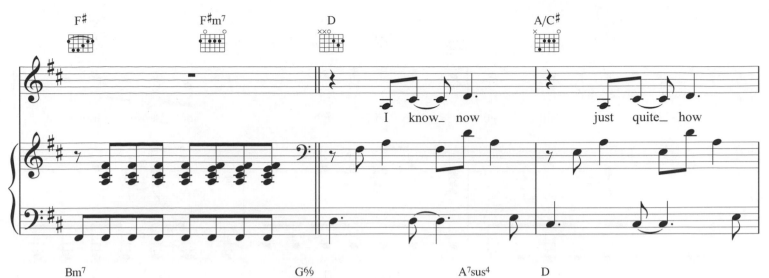

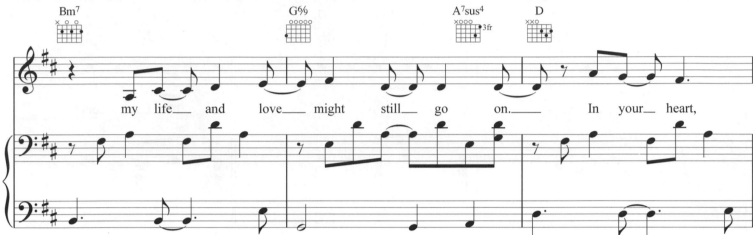

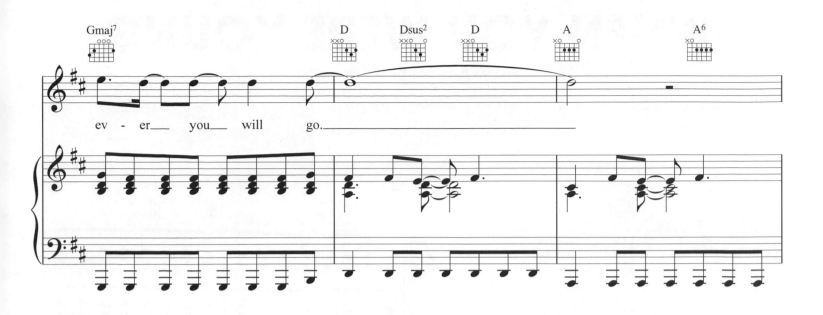

ev - er___ you___ will go._____

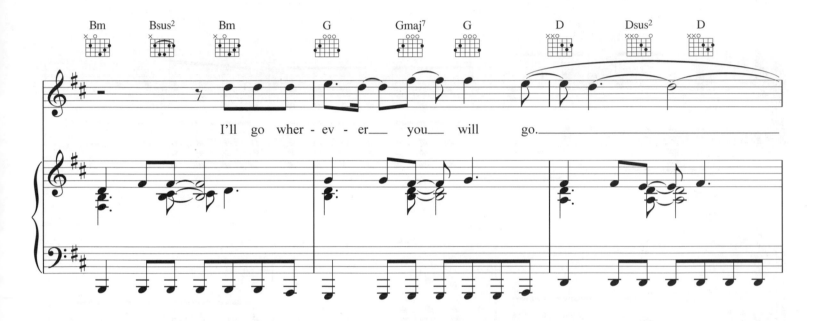

I'll go wher - ev - er___ you___ will go._____

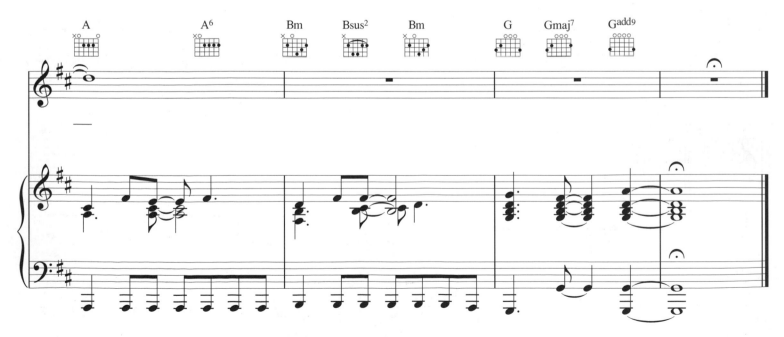

WHEN YOU WERE YOUNG

Words & Music by Justin Currie

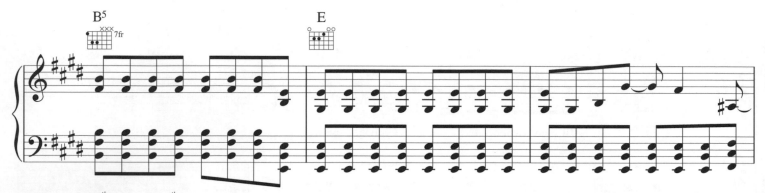

1, 3. You sit there_ in your heart-ache. Wait-ing on some
2. Can we climb_ this moun-tain? I don't know. High-er now than ev-

215

216

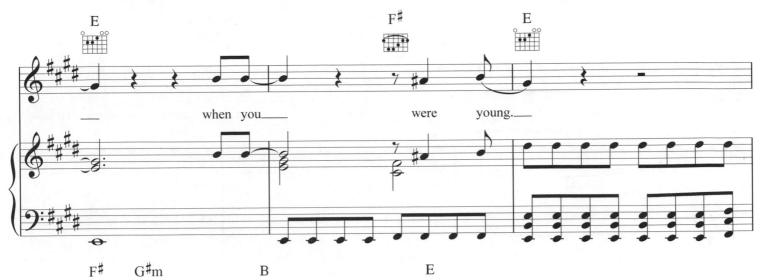

when you___ were young.___

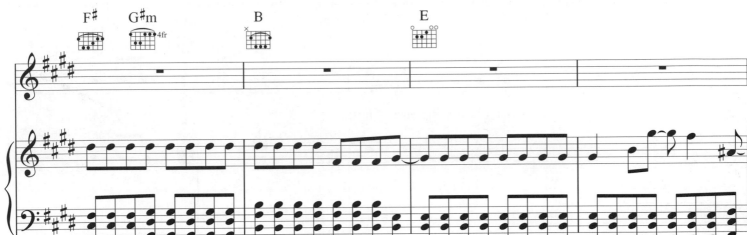

They say the

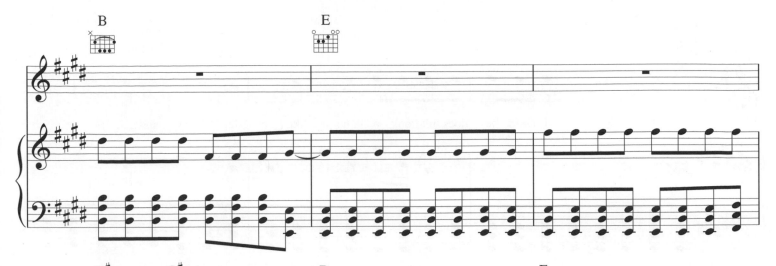

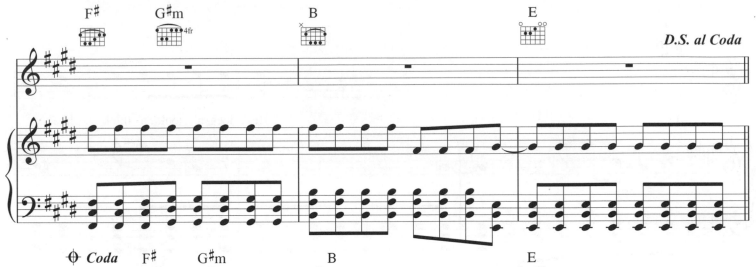

D.S. al Coda

(Talks like a gen-tle-man. Like you im-ag-ined.) When you

were young.

WONDERWALL

Words & Music by Noel Gallagher

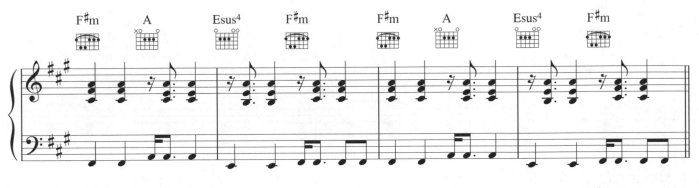

To-day is gon-na be the day that they're gon-na throw it back to you,__

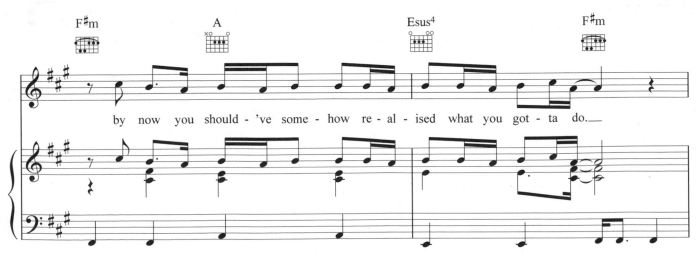

by now you should-'ve some-how re-al-ised what you got-ta do.__

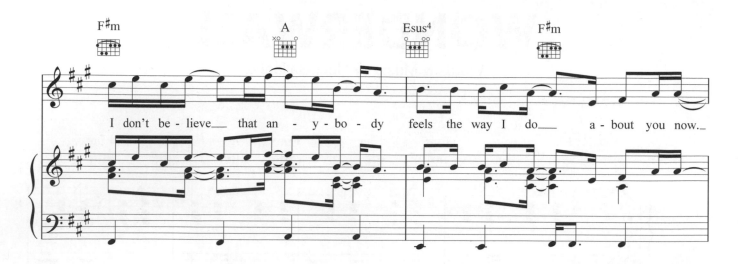

I don't be-lieve__ that an - y-bo-dy feels the way I do__ a-bout you now._

1. Back - beat the word was on the street that the fi - re in your heart is out._
2. To - day was gon - na be the day but they'll nev - er throw it back to you._

I'm sure you've heard it all be - fore but you nev - er real - ly had a doubt._
By now you should-'ve some - how re - al - ised what you're not to do._

222

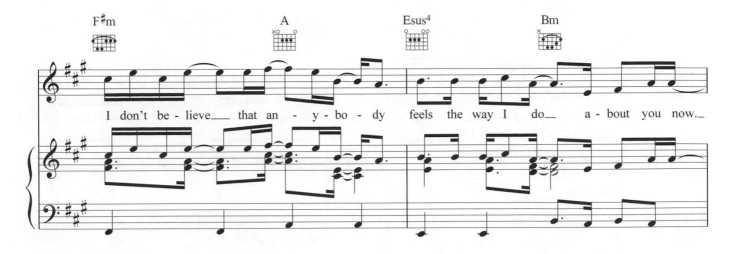

I don't be-lieve___ that an - y - bo - dy feels the way I do___ a - bout you now.___

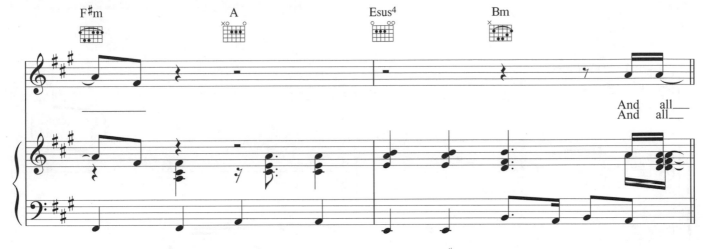

And all___
And all___

___ the roads___ we have___ to walk___ are wind - ing   and all_
___ the roads___ that lead___ you there___ were wind - ing   and all_

___ the lights___ that lead___ us there___ are blind - ing.)
___ the lights___ that light___ the way___ are blind - ing.)

There are ma - ny things___ that I___ would like to say to you___ but I don't know how,___

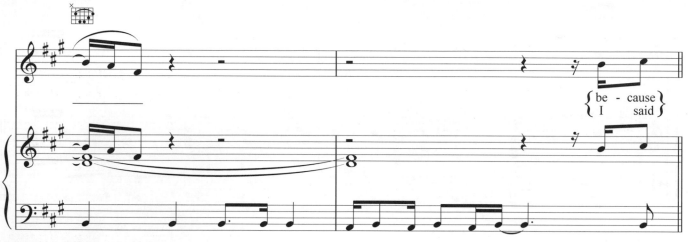

{be - cause}
{I said}

may - be___   you're gon - na be the one that

saves me,___   and af - ter all___

may - be_____ you're gon - na be the one that

(Continue as instr.)

Repeat ad lib.

saves me_____ you're gon - na be the one that

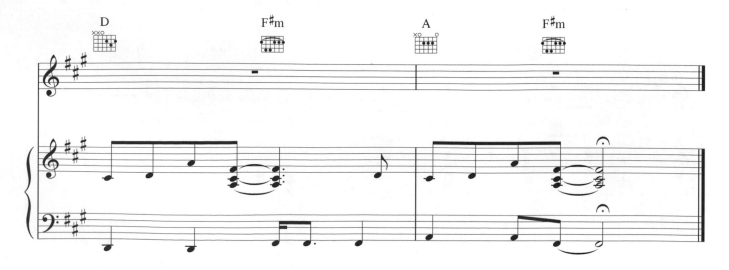

You Had Me

Words & Music by Francis White, Joss Stone, Betty Wright & W. Stoker

I don't want you here, mess-ing with my mind.

I've real - ised in time that my eyes are not blind.

I've seen it be - fore; I'm tak - ing back my life.

You swore_ you had con-trol of it;___ when I___ stepped back,_ you slipped on your_ sup-ply._

You had me,___ you lost me,___ you're wast-ed,___ you cost_ me._

YOU GIVE ME SOMETHING

Words & Music by Francis White & James Morrison

235

Bringing you the words and the music

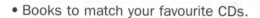